DRIVING US INSANE

DRIVING

US INSANE

A YEAR IN THE FAST LANE WITH JEREMY KLAXON

A Parody

Atlantic
Books

From: AA Roadkill <aa.roadkill@gmail.com>
Date: Tue, 13 Jul 2010 14:46:24 +0100
To: Publishing Director <publishingdirector@groveatlantic.co.uk>
Subject: Jazza's potboiler

FOREWORD
by A.A. Roadkill

"Speak Truth to Power". That, of course, is the motto of the British Broadcasting Corporation, but it might just as easily be that of my old friend and fellow scribe Jeremy Klaxon, because Jeremy – just plain Jazza to his friends – has always done that: spoken truth to power. Sometimes this has involved him in controversy. Sometimes the Powers-that-be do not want to hear the truth. Ramblers; men who play golf; Koreans; Guardian readers; wimmin'; the French; footballers who care perhaps immoderately for their looks; Romanians in shawls; anyone on a bicycle; American fattists; the Scotch; people who believe in global warming; chaps who wear towels on their heads; Germans; Labour-voters; those of an alternative sexual orientation; comprehensive-school educated young men who favour hooded sweatshirts; people from the Midlands; Belgian-based legislators; council officials in hi-viz tabards; the elderly, the halt and the lame; Peugeot drivers; the French (again); ugly girls. These are just a few of the sorts of people who haven't taken kindly to Jazza telling it the way he sees it.

Indeed these "powers" have long sought to silence Jazza. They've set out to plug that pure sweet bubbling source of reason and to silence the clarion call of one of the most distinct – and distinctive – voices in the land. Sometimes they've managed it. Sometimes, by the misappropriation of the various instruments available to them – such as the Committee for Racial Equality, the Criminal Prosecution Service, the libel courts and the BBC Executive Board – they have triumphed. Sometimes they've succeeded in gagging the Bard of Bradford; the Chronicler of Chipping Norton; the Godalming

Gazetteer; the Manx Magus. Sometimes his columns are spiked. Sometimes his television programme, so lovingly crafted by experts well-versed in every nuance of the forty-minute light entertainment format, is edited in post-production with what George Orwell might have described as a "heavy" hand. Sometimes the humble viewer – the man in the street, the man waiting for the Clapham Omnibus that is sadly mired in traffic, the man with the wheeze and the sweat dribbling down his back because it is so goddamned hot – hasn't heard everything the Great Man has had to say.

Which is a shame.

For only by seeing the man "in the round" can anyone really understand what a colossal contribution he has made – and continues to make – to the cultural climate of this once great nation (now sadly overrun by those whom Jazza might describe as "sag-teated carbonists"). Only by seeing the day-to-day struggles of everybody's favourite curly-haired multi-millionaire as he sets out to make room for himself – not just in the drive of his mansion where cars are parked as "thick as autumnal leaves that strow the brooks in Vallombrosa", but in our country's cultural headspace – can the reader begin to grasp the enormity of that input. Not for nothing has he become known as the unthinking man's Richard Dawkins.

Driving Us Insane: A Year in the Fast Lane with Jeremy Klaxon, Presenter of TV's BottomGear gives us a glimpse of that contribution, and with it the insight we require to form a proper opinion of our country's most singular cultural icon. By following him through the various vicissitudes he faces throughout the year, and by reading of the methods he uses to overcome the slings and arrows that outrageous fortune sends his way, I hope you will come to see – as I have – what a giant of a man he was, is, and will be.

This then is his life, and you are welcome to it.

A.A. Roadkill,
August, 2010

FRIDAY 1ST JANUARY

Rammond says starting a diary on January the first is
like driving a Ford Mondeo Titanium X saloon. Now I
don't know what he means by that but I can tell he means
it as a joke, because he laughs, and afterwards says 'as
you do', as he always does, so I know I have to go one
better.

'No, Rammond,' I say, 'it's like driving a - ', but then
the words escape me. What is it like? What possible
relevance to car driving has keeping a diary?

'It's like driving a what, Jeremy?' he asks, and I can
imagine his eyes are all goggly and demonic.

But I still don't know.

'A Range Rover?' I try.

'A Range Rover?' he scoffs, and then he says he has to
go and talk to his agent about doing a voiceover for a
television series on squirrel-culling in Kosovo.

'I meant a Range Rover Discovery,' I say into my
silent iPhone gizmo, but of course, Rammond's hung up, 'as
you do'.

Why did I ever give Rammond the job in the first place?

It was all right to begin with because he knew his
place, but then he had his crash and now his books are
all over Budgens and whenever you turn the telly on,
there he is, goofing around like a Korean, with an access-
all-areas ticket to Crufts.

And where exactly is Kosovo? Does anyone know?

Exactly. I rest my case. It's one of those comical
made-up countries, isn't it, where everybody's called
Goran, and come the local saint's day they ritually
catch the tips of their penises in their fly zips while
chucking live donkeys from tower block walkways.

EUROPE: EAST OF MERCEDES

RUSSIA
Footballist oligarchs
Maria Sharapova
(non-lesbianist tennis player)
Vodka
Borsch

Cars that are less shit than they were (following German invasion)), Beer, Stag weekends, Tennis-playing lesbianists

KOSOVO

KOSOVO

POLAND
Root vegetables, Plumbers, Vodka

CZECH REPUBLIC

UKRAINE
Communism, Vodka, Borsch

KOSOVO

KOSOVO

ITALY

TRANSYLVANIA
Vampire communists, Cheeky Girls, Gymnasts

KOSOVO

YUGOSERBATIA

Ferraris, Lamborghinis, men with handbags, Women on time-delay fuses

People called 'Slobodan' Violent Bosnosexualists Slivovitz

Like most of Europe, basically.

But you see, here's the thing: I can't fire Rammond from *BottomGear*. And I can't fire him from *BottomGear* because of what happened on that awful night in Germany.

MONDAY 4TH JANUARY

So here we go. 4th January. The first day of the rest of my life. *BottomGear*'s producer Amil rings after lunch to tell me the ratings are in and even though it's a repeat from two years ago, our Christmas Special was watched by seven million people, twenty-six of whom rang the BBC to complain about me using the phrase 'turkey-bark'.

No, I didn't know what that meant either, but Zafira, my wife-and-manager, has given me a little crib sheet on which she has written a list of words I have to use to stir things up.

Now apparently a turkey-bark is a type of fart.

No, really. But it isn't just any old fart. No, a turkey-bark turns out to be the Bugatti Veyron (POA) of farts, if you will, because, ladies and gentlemen, just like Santa Claus and James Might, it comes but once a year, and even then only at Christmas.

You see, a turkey-bark is that special fart you let out after you've had your Christmas dinner with your in-laws. You're driving back through country lanes and you're a bit pissed and you roll onto one buttock and let it out in all its turkey-flavoured glory, don't you, and for once your wife doesn't say anything because she's snoring gently with her head against the heated dashboard.

Anyway, I was talking about the climate control on the new Range Rover and I had to say that one among many

WORDS TO STIR THINGS UP

bean juice

choad

cooze

Copenhagen capon

front bottom

fuckmuffin

fucksauce

furry donut

ginch

golden hoop

pocket frog

queef

snapping turtle

stoat

trouser cakes

trouser cough

turkey-bark

twange

vag

wolf pussy

JEZ – please don't forget to look at this list!!!   Zafira xxx

of its advantages is that it has special witchcrafty sensors that detect any nutrients in the air, shall we say, extracts them and replaces them with the smell of, I dunno, lavender or fresh coffee. Rammond was scripted to ask if it got rid of *all* odours, and I had to say, yes, even if you let out a 'turkey-bark'.

As I said 'turkey-bark', Natasha - Amil's assistant, ✓✓✓✓✓ and a girl whom you most definitely would, if you had a yes! spare half hour and a pack of Lurpak at room temperature - held up a sign to the audience that said LAUGH and no

10

one did, except Rammond, even though he can't EVEN READ YET.

It's true that the crowd was a bit uncomfortable because for reasons I don't claim to understand - something to do with the baggy-breasted raisin-counters who run the BBC, no doubt - we were shooting the Christmas Special in the middle of July, and Amil had made all the bald blokes who pay to watch the show dress up in Christmas jumpers and reindeer hats and so on.

Anyway, under the heat of the lights they began sweating like blond boys in a Turkish barracks. In the end we had to dust their heads with talcum powder to dim the glare, but it only got worse when the bus from HMP Holloway arrived with all the women we hire to make the show look less blokey.

Each of these women from HMP Holloway is butcher than James and Rammond and me put together, and sometimes when we watch the footage afterwards I see them staring at my back and I feel like one of those barrels of pork fat the French navy used to sail with, the ones with holes drilled into the sides, put on the quarter deck to offer the sailors - or 'matelots' as we call them - an alternative to sodomizing one another. They all caught venereal disease and died as a result, of course, but what do you expect from the French?

GRAISSE DE PORC

INSÉREZ VOTRE MEMBRE ICI

So what with the heat and the Christmas jumpers and reindeer horns, all the bald sweaty blokes and the felonious lesbians had their minds on other things, and none of them was going to be fobbed off with a pre-scripted laugh-along.

So when no one laughed the first time I said turkey-bark, Amil asked me to do the bit again. This time, though, he asked me to pull 'my face' to camera as I said it.

I didn't understand what he meant.

My face is my face. I don't know anyone who consciously pulls a face, except me that is, when I am pretending to be a woman having an orgasm. Though perhaps the less said about that the better.

Amil kept going on about me looking mournful and droopy as I normally do when I make one of these jokes. And then when I still didn't get it, he said, 'Oh all right then, just pull your normal monkey-scrotum face.'

And that's what got the laugh.

Which brings me nicely to my point that whatever day you start a diary it is always the first day of the rest of your life. And as someone with even more time on their hands than a Romanian lorry driver on a cross-Channel ferry once said: keep a diary and it will keep you. Or as Zafira says, it comes in handy if kids stop buying my new *Thriller* DVD and those *BottomGear* Top Trumps cards.

THURSDAY 7TH JANUARY

Drive up towards the studio to talk to Amil and Rammond about future stars in our reasonably priced car. I say 'towards' the studio because as usual the M40 is completely chockablock with Peugeot drivers driving as if they have their nipples in mousetraps, ready to snap down at the slightest sign of life.

I mean, what's the point of sitting there in neutral? Don't they know how to drive?

In the end I have to make a 'conference call' on my iPhone while sitting in the fast lane with the nose of the Range Rover rammed up the jacksy of a Winnebago-style mobile home called a Kip DeLux.

Who chose that name, I wonder?

A Capuchin monkey would have come up with a better name, if you'd given it a functioning biro and a gram of cocaine. *√√√ use this on BottomGear*

Amil and Natasha are meeting in the production offices at the BBC and they've moved a speaker onto the table so they can hear my suggestions. That is until Rammond comes in. I hear him swing the chair around so that he can sit on it backwards 'as you do' and then he puts one of his butterscotch-coloured leather blousons over the loudspeaker.

I have to shout to make myself heard, and even then no one hears me.

'JAMES BLUNT! MICHAEL FISH! URI GELLER! TERRY WAITE!'

People in other cars nearby are staring at me through their windows, and for a moment I think they've recognized me, television's Jeremy Klaxon, but then I catch a glimpse of myself in the backlit leather-trimmed vanity mirror. It is like seeing a very purple-faced

MY DESERT ISLAND DISCS:

~~Yours is no Disgrace (Yes)~~

Your Song (Elton John)

Behind Blue Eyes (The Who)

Night Moves (Bob Seger)

~~The Final Countdown (Europe)~~

Time (Pink Floyd)

Get Ready (Temptations)

Make me Smile (Come Up & See Me)
(Steve Harley)

~~The Lady in Red (Chris de Burgh)~~

Heroes (David Bowie)

Solsbury Hill (Peter Gabriel)

shouty man with eyebrows like an emperor penguin, veins throbbing in his temple, a mop of pubic hair on top, heading for what looks like an aneurism.

Calm myself by slipping the disc of my *Desert Islands Discs* choice into the CD player, and when I get to the song 'Night Moves', I start singing aloud:

'Tight Pants, Points, hardly renowned, she was a black haired beauty with big dark eyes, And points of her own sitting way up high, way up firm and high.'

That is in my all-time top five songs about nipples, I can exclusively reveal.

Sue Lawley. Back then you wouldn't have said no, would you? But now: bit of a boiler.

Like most Greek women.

Not that she is Greek.

By the time I reach the M40-M25 intersection I've missed the meeting and when Rammond finally takes his blouson off the phone in the office I hear them all agreeing that the 'old' format needed 'tweaking', and that Rammond - RAMMOND! - was right to suggest a 'shake-up'.

'COME BACK!' I shout, 'JOHN NETTLES OWES ME A FAVOUR!'

Tellingly, the only answer I get is the sound of the office door closing and tumbleweed rolling in the wind. Or rather the low rumble of the Range Rover's 450 bhp V-12 engine. The Range Rover is a beautiful ride, though, statesmanlike, regal, and superbly upholstered, and I can confirm that it can hold the road at speeds of anything up to - oooh - ten mph. Furthermore I will say this for it; if you suddenly tweak the steering-wheel and power across the hard shoulder and up over three fields of winter barley, a school playground and a Tesco's parking lot so that you can get onto a slip road that will take you home, the Range Rover is as responsive as a lark - in a James Dyson Dual Cyclone bagless vacuum cleaner. ✓✓✓

Another one for BottomGear!

FRIDAY 22ND JANUARY

It is deadline day for my column, but I can't think of a single thing to say that I haven't already said a million times. Normally that doesn't stop me filing my 1000 words, but today I can't get into the groove, so Zafira my-wife-and-manager tells me to go to the pub for a pint.

It's only a couple of hundred yards to The Lamb and Foreskin, but I get in the Range Rover and drive. Walking is for Ethiopians and postmen, and these days most of them have outsourced their jobs to Kenyans or Thai ladyboys.

Down in the village all the old locals have been bought out of the cottages their ancestors built from

spit and potato peel by men called Nigel. Now they live in asbestos prefabs up by the plague pits, where it is not so much *Lark Rise to Candleford* as *The Hills Have Eyes*, *1*, *2* and *3*. They all keep devil dogs and brew their own alcohol in tin baths and on Tuesdays they send their inbred Cyclops children to vandalize the hanging baskets by the war memorial.

And who can blame them, I say. I mean, think about it.

Who needs flowers? They make you sneeze in spring and they inspire poets to tell us things about themselves we don't want to know.

At the weekend you can hardly move in the village for 4x4s and people-carriers and it usually takes me longer to find a parking space than it did to sit my A-levels. For once I am with the American National Rifle Association on this one, though: you can't blame a car or a gun for what people choose to do with it, can you? You can't blame Mr Heckler or Mr Koch if someone uses one of their very fine submachine guns to massacre their classmates, can you? Just as you can't blame a car if someone drives it head on at 60 mph into a bandstand of retired lollipop

√√√√
must make
these points
on my next
appearance
on the David
Dimbleby
show!!

ladies playing the theme from the A-Team on the village green.

YOU MIGHT AS WELL TRY AND BAN JELLY.

Anyway in the pub I order a pint and a packet of crisps. The barmaid is new and can't find them. She looks up. She looks down. I look up (her skirt is short). I look down (her top is low). I let her see my key fob, but she does not recognize it for what it is, ignorant little minx. Now I'll have to lure her into the car park so that she can see me get into the Range Rover and know that I am carrying some serious wad.

Her eyes are too close together and her name-tag reads Svetlana and I think we all know what I'm thinking.

What is it with the Poles? Why are their eyes so close together?

I don't know the answer to that, obviously, but it

Svetlana admiring my key fob

brings me nicely onto my point: if we are to believe Darwin's theory of the survival of the fittest, and I think we all do, then shouldn't they all be dead?

You see, here's the thing: with such close-set eyes, your average Pole has to have virtual tunnel vision.

Now I know what you're thinking: virtual tunnel vision is no bad thing, and you'd be right. Right, that is, if you only wanted to spend your life making potato soup, say, or raping your own livestock.

17

But what if you can't spend your whole life sexually
assaulting farm animals? *Note to self*

Come-to-bed eyes

What if you are
sent to safeguard
a frontier, say?
What if you are
sent to safeguard
a frontier that
borders on lands
belonging to
wider-eyed,
more aggressive
neighbours?
Well, I'll
tell you.
What happens
is that while you are peering down the road thinking
longingly of your father's ewes, a mechanized division
of wide-eyed fanatics in grey uniforms and huge panzer
tanks will flank your little hut, drive all the way to
your capital city, and burn it down.

Logic demands, then, that a race of people with such
close-set eyes would soon be 'amalgamated' into this
nation of wider-eyed men and women.

But they're not.

And why not?

Because of the so-called thousand-year EuroReich.

No, really. You see, along with almost everything
else that is pleasurable in life - public masturbation,
dwarfism and suttee - our so-called self-appointed
masters in Brussels have banned war in Europe.

Think about it. Along with gratuitously teasing

Americans, waterboarding Bill Oddie, smearing Keira Knightley in honey, war in Europe joins the list of things WE'RE NO LONGER ALLOWED TO DO.

Of course this means that anyone can drive from Calais to the Bosphorus without a toilet break - which is no bad thing - but it also means that it is now ILLEGAL to attack Poland.

Which is no GOOD thing. I mean, think about it. Poland.

Its inhabitants are named after black stuff you put on your shoes, and I don't mean polish.

Or perhaps, on second thoughts, I do.

Anyway, as it turned out this girl wasn't Polish but came from Chipping Norton, North Oxfordshire's barbecue sauce capital, and here's a chilling thing: she tells me the only way to get a job in this country these days is to pretend to be Polish.

But what struck me most of all was that her perfume was almost as strong as Rammond's. (Another reason Might won't share a room with the BBC's smallest life form

PLEASURABLE THINGS BANNED BY THE THOUSAND-YEAR EUROREICH: THE SHORTLIST

1. Dwarfism
2. Waterboarding Bill Oddie
3. Suttee
4. Smearing Keira Knightley in honey
5. War in Europe
6. Public masturbation

apart from Basil Brush: he wears an aftershave called
'Joop!'). And it gives me a brilliant idea for my
column.

Perfume: what's the point? Everybody knows that bacon
is the best smell in the world.

I ask Zafira if she prefers the smell of perfume or
bacon.

'Frying bacon is maybe good smell, but uncooked bacon
smell of Denmark.'

Denmark!

She laughs.

'Do column on Denmark,' she says, as if my columns
just make themselves up. To prove her point though, she
looks in the computer for the column that I wrote for
last week's paper in which I asked what the point of
Norway was, and she fiddles with it, changing Oslo for

NIGEL'S BARN
CONVERSION

Neeeigh

Copenhagen and so on, and pings it off to my editor who waves it straight through to the printers, and after I've spoken to him on the phone ('lovely job, Jez') I sit back and look out of the French windows and watch two horses mating in a field.

WEDNESDAY 3RD FEBRUARY

Bloody James.

Last week's meeting would have been different if he'd been there, of course, but James is on holiday. In fact, James has gone to the only country where Rammond isn't king - or at least princeling - of the daytime telly schedules. James has gone to the only place left in the whole wide world where *BottomGear* isn't shown on a rolling loop morning noon and night. James has gone, ladies and gentlemen, to Burma.

Yes, Burma, where people really do wear banana leaves instead of clothes and where warm devilled cat is the national delicacy. Burma, where they rub noses with one another to say hello, or I love you, or your house is on fire.

Burma, where - actually, where is Burma?

Anyway, James charged the flights to the BBC and told the Men in Suits he was scouting a new location in which to film a *BottomGear* Challenge. Not that they'll believe him of course, because if there is one thing they know about James Might, it's that he hates *BottomGear* Challenges.

James hates them even more than I do.

James would rather have his testicles chopped off and served up on a plate with a side dish of refried pimento beans than go on another challenge. James would rather

√√√ Worth an airing on
BottomGear?

James takes a shit

have a sharpened telegraph pole pushed up his anus, without any lubricant, sideways.

James would - well, you get my point.

But he has to do these challenges, and why?

Because I insisted they were put in his contract.

You see, when he first came slinking around the BBC offices in his homosexualist shirts and his pot belly and floppy locks looking for a job I couldn't quite believe it. Seeing him in the video-intercom was like seeing a cat taking a shit on my lawn. I wanted to bang on the window and shoo him off. 'Get away!' I wanted to cry.

But then he put it to me, and he put it to me quite persuasively, that he was - apart from Quentin Willson, of course - the only man on telly, who could make me look good.

He's an odd character for a motoring show, I agree. People think he is a very slow, careful driver, but not a bit of it. He is trying, honest he is. It is just that his feet are so long they're too big for the accelerator. He has feet like Gollum, only longer, and instead of Captain Slow, Zafira calls him Sideshow James, after the Simpsons character with shoes a yard long. He has shoes like Swiss rolls. He has shoes like those salamis you see in so-called authentic delis.

Anyway, for all those reasons I took him on.

Which brings me nicely back to my point. The real

problem with the challenges is not all the time-wasting nor the stupid and pointless nature of them, nor even the lame set-ups or the mugging to camera (my monkey-scrotum face again).

No, the real problem with the challenges is that I have to share a room, WITH RAMMOND.

You see, after the Road Trip Special around the spectacularly fat states of America, while I was recording *Klaxon's Top Ten Turkeys* (my new DVD, available from all good bookshops, RRP £14.99), I took my eye off the ball. I didn't notice that James's contract was up and that he had it written into his new contract that he would never have to share a room with Rammond, ever again.

So now clause 4 subsection 2b paragraph 8 - or whatever - of James's contract states that not only must he have the honeymoon suite of whichever hotel we are staying in, it must also come with a pair of freshly pressed silk pyjamas (size L, covered in a 'non-gaudy' paisley pattern), a bottle of San Pellegrino *frizzante*, and no Rammond.

Which leaves me to bunk up with the smallest man in broadcasting, apart, that is, from Jeanette Tough of the Krankies, though to be fair she's not really in broadcasting any more. Which is a shame.

To begin with it was like being back at school, with the smells and the picking of feet and all the things you usually enjoy, but then, after lights-out, it got a bit odd.

In fact I began to see why Might insists on his clause.

You see, Rammond doesn't just talk in his sleep,

23

he shouts in his sleep. He shouts words like 'anus' and 'Bristol Siddeley Orpheus'. He shouts words like 'Deploy Parachute' and he shouts words like 'I'm coming, Melinda!'

More than that, though, he gets up in the middle of the night. He gets up in the middle of the night and he paces around the room, and while he's doing this, he is always wearing tight white pants, and his eyes glow in the dark, like someone from that ghost-hunting show they keep repeating on Dave-ja Vu when they should be showing *BottomGear*. I think he has nightmares about being put in a tube and forced up Richard Gere's backside.

Zafira my wife-and-manager thinks that odd little necklace he wears must have been given to him by a voodoo priest, too. 'Why else he wear?' she asks. And do you know what? I think she may have a point.

TUESDAY 9TH FEBRUARY

Slept badly, and after breakfast (dark chocolate Bounty bar and a can of Coca Cola) I have to play an hour on *Call of Duty: Modern Warfare 4* to get me in the mood for it. Then I get into the first car I can find on my drive that is pointing in the right direction.

I mean what's the point of reversing?

When you're a child you reverse, yes, that's true, but you also wet your bed and enjoy Farley's rusks, and, like

NOoo...!!!

24

roll-up cigarettes and masturbating over *The Razzler*, you should grow out of it. The only people who still reverse are the Italians, and that's because their girlfriends won't sleep with them until they're married, and then when they do get married, they explode into great fat Easter puddings.

So it isn't surprising they're all trying to wind the clock back.

This car is a silver Audi RS6 Avant with red leather seats with the keys in the ignition and a big START button on the dashboard.

I turn it over, ooh listen to that engine! It is like dipping your testicles in a bowl of warm pasta and thinking of that girl who used to do the adverts for Flake.

√√√√
maybe not one
for Question
Time

The engine is a massive eleventy million bhp and I manage to get up to 60 mph, BEFORE I GET OUT OF THE DRIVE.

On the radio the Department of Fretting Needlessly (the DoFN) reveals that this winter has been the coldest on record. Instead of seeing this as a good thing, the gusset-botherers at the BBC wheel out some sag-chested old boiler to warn us that the old and poor will die because of it.

√√
Ha, Ha!

As if this is bad news!

Having actually been to the North Pole I can tell you that we don't know what the cold actually is. There aren't many poor people there, I can tell you. Mind you, there isn't much of anything around there, except polar bears, and there are fewer of them each year, thank God.

Anyway, as if then to RAM the point home about it being cold, some dipwit weather forecaster comes on and predicts heavy snow!

It is always a mistake to be a weather forecaster and forecast snow.

This is because it never snows in London.

The reason it never snows in London? It is not, as those stupid environophiles will have you believe, that human activity has increased the local temperature by up to four degrees, but because the rest of the country - except for a few bits around Manchester - is in a huge frost-pocket.

Another thing I've noticed about weathergirls is how quickly they get pregnant. They come on, you think ah, a new face, and for a week or so you think to yourself maybe I would, maybe I wouldn't, and then within a week or two you discover someone has! They become the shape of one of their beloved cumulus clouds and despite the layer of slap as thick as a hubcap, they flush on and off like a lighthouse on the blink for a month or two, and then they push off to enjoy a few years' R & R at the licence payers' expense.

Leaving us with Siân Bloody Lloyd.

They like it up 'em, apparently

Well thanks very much.

I expect she's perfectly good company, though.

TUESDAY 16TH FEBRUARY

To the BBC again. Amil sends a runner down to fetch me from the security. She's basically a child and talks like an Australian, but without their natural sunny charm.

'Sorry we're running late?' the girlchild says, 'But Amil was in a meeting?' It is as if she is asking me a question but I know it isn't one.

This is just the way children speak these days. There is a fancy phrase for it: interrogative uplift or something, but sorry, that's bollocks, if you'll pardon the expletive.

The real reason they speak like that is that they are taught by lesbians.

Yes. Lesbians.

You see, lesbians have very short attention spans.

No, really. I don't mean that being a lesbian gives you a short attention span, though that may also be true, but rather that it is having a very short attention span that turns you into lesbian, and here's why.

Learning how another gender's body works requires time, patience and concentration, doesn't it? You remember those first heterosexual adolescent fumbles behind the bike shed?

How unsatisfying were they?

CARS FOR LESBIANS:
THE SHORT LIST

1. 2CV (no reason)
2. Toyota (not) Priapic
3. Nissan Sapphic
4. Reva G-Spot
5. Fiat Straddle

A lesbian teacher arrives at school

If they were anything like mine, well, you'll understand why I took up an early interest in cars.

But it stands to reason that it is much easier to fumble someone whose body parts are similar to your own, doesn't it? You don't have to put in all the wearisome hours learning to achieve satisfactory results because you can be pretty sure that if their body is anything like yours, then they will like what you like, and a few seconds later, *voilà!*, as the French say (they would, wouldn't they?) and Bob's your uncle.

Or aunt, in this case.

My point is that people who don't have the attention span to learn how to satisfy the opposite sex always end up gay.

Now for one reason or another most schoolteachers are lesbians.

Therefore most schoolteachers do not have long attention spans.

Therefore they cannot teach our children to have long attention spans.

Therefore our children do not have long attention spans.

Therefore their sentences need to be short because by the time they get to the end of long sentences, they will have forgotten what they were talking about at the start of the sentence.

Therefore all lefty beardy lesbian teachers should be fired. ✓✓✓ *Up yours, Channel Four!!!*

MONDAY 22ND FEBRUARY

A list of the world's three most depressing words:

1. London Wetlands Centre
2. Last polar bear
3. Not tonight, Jeremy
4. Janet Street-Porter
5. Jenni bloody Murray

WEDNESDAY 24TH FEBRUARY

Amil isn't interested in anyone on my list of Stars for the Reasonably Priced Car!

He doesn't care that the list includes Danny Glover, Trish from that afternoon telly show (Zafira's idea: she met her at the Chipping Norton Bring-and-Buy sale), Michael Flatley, both members of Steely Dan, General Sir Peter Edgar de la Cour de la Billière, KCB, KBE, DSO, MC & Bar, MSN & txtspk, Kelly LeBrock, and, as they say, many more.

Rammond pops in with his clothes pulled from the back of an 18-year-old cowpoke and hair he's borrowed from Rod Hull's Emu, dyed to match the colour of straw. There is something demonic about his bush-baby eyes this morning, and I recall Zafira's suspicion that he has sold his soul to Baron Samedi.

He shakes my hand with that curious young person's

grip of his, even though I know he is two years older
than me, calls me 'dawg' and punches me on the shoulder,
leaving a skidmark of Joop! on the jacket that Zafira
bought me at Austin Reed.

He says he can't stop, got a meeting about some new
kids' show he's been asked to do.

When he's gone Amil tells me that we're going to use
BottomGear's influence 'for good'. 'For good?' I ask.
'Yes Jeremy. For too long we have ignored our role as
brand ambassadors and blah blah blah blah.' I stick my
fingers in my ears and pull that really horrible face I
make when I want to suggest a woman is having an orgasm.

Through the tips of my fingers I can hear Amil banging
on about how this new segment could be the solution
to the world's seemingly intractable conflicts, and how
BottomGear could bring peace to the world and blah blah
blah.

What he has in mind, it turns out, is to get two
guests onto the show each week, both of whom hate each
other's guts, and then get them to race around the track
in equally reasonably priced cars and whoever
wins, wins.

So, for example, the first stars - if we
can call them that any more - will
be the Dalai Lama and someone
called Hu Jintao. For once I was
too ashamed of my ignorance and

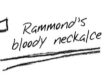

Rammond's
bloody neckalce

don't ask who Hu Jintao is,
just in case it is one of
Amil's relations, so I ask
the girlchild to get me
onto the interwebby thing.

It turns out that the
interwebs is not just
for looking at glossy
upskirt pictures of
Dame Keira Knightley -
though that is obviously
its primary function
- but also a mine of
useless information on
Hu Jintao. I discover
that this Hu Jintao
is: a) a man, and b)
what they call the
Paramount Leader of
the People's Republic of China,
holding the titles of General Secretary of the... Well,
he is king of All China and everything Chinese basically,
which probably includes my local Chinese restaurant, the
Beijing Gourmet, in Chipping Norton, though, obviously, I'd
have to check.

Amil's idea is to get these two to race one another
around our track and whoever wins gets to call Tibet
their own, and no more silly messing about.

It's a trial by combat without the combat and it makes
me wonder if we ought not to give them guns too, so that
they can take pot shots at one another from their racing
cars? Or hammers? Or laser beams? Something like that.

NEWSREADERS WHO
SHOULD BE BOND GIRLS:
THE SHORTLIST

1. Fiona Bruce
2. Kate Silverton
3. Selina Scott
4. Angela Rippon
5. Tom Bradby
6. Natasha Kaplinsky
7. Sophie Raworth

Amil says not, that the Health and Safety Reichsbummers won't go for it, and so once again the Powers That Be crush us under the crêpe soles of their organic suede shoes.

WEDNESDAY 3RD MARCH

Woken in the early hours by a text from James sent from the airport in Rangoon. He's coming home via Sri Lanka and did I 'wnt 2 go 1/2s' on some so called 'conflict dinosaur eggs' he is going to smuggle back into the country? I tell him no.

Immediate response on column about the stupidity of forecasting snow and the preservation of Poland as an exercise in biblical futility by the thousand-year Eurocratic Union. The chairman of the local Conservative branch rings at ten wondering if he can 'stop by for a chat'. 'Loved your column, by the way Jez,' he says. 'Nice to find someone singing from the same hymn sheet.' Ten minutes later a man with an unlikely name rings from something called UKIP, wondering whether we might get together some time in the coming week, 'just for a chat, you understand, hehehehehe'. Then someone from something called the English Democratic Party rings to invite me down to the pub at lunchtime for 'a pint and a Castella'.

It all sounds a bit Monty Python, of course, but what Amil was saying the other day has stuck in my mind. I'm beginning to see that it is no longer enough to sit on the sidelines and pass exactly 1000 words of drivel a week. Perhaps it is a midlife crisis, but I find myself looking at all the cars sitting in my drive, waiting for review, and my heart sinks. Yes. They are cars. They have wheels and so on, but really, aren't they just cars? How many more ways are there to describe them? Blah blah blah understeer blah blah blah flappy paddle gearbox.

Sometimes I almost envy Quentin Willson. I envy the way he doesn't bother even to try to make cars sound interesting. He just sits there in his polo neck looking like the poster boy for a harelip charity campaign and he doesn't have to say things like 'I'd rather be in this, than in Farrah Fawcett Majors' - I mean before she died of cancer, of course - or 'this is better than waxing Myleene Klass'.

✓✓✓✓✓ Yes!!!

All the others have got something else to do: Rammond with his kids' shows, James with his dinosaur egg smuggling business, but what do I have? All right, five luxury cars in the garage and a house in the Isle of Man, but what else?

If I could get into politics, what would Rammond say then?

So I mooch along to the pub to find the chap from the English Democratic Forum for Change Party - or whatever - sitting by the fire wearing a blazer covered with dandruff, a poppy in the lapel with a glass of bitter on the table in front of him. The strange thing is that when I see him I am sure I've met him before, but where?

The memory has gone clean out of my tiny little mind.

'Klaxon,' he grins, standing up. His teeth are like those corn snacks they give tourists to eat in Spain and

he's no taller than a Triumph Herald, but when he shakes
my hand his grip is like the disc brake on a Bugatti
Veyron (again), only very slightly puffier.

'Trubshawe,' he says. 'Ron Trubshawe. Major, Royal
Electrical and Mechanical Engineers, Retired. Glad you
could make it. Fancy a gargle?'

I nod. I still can't place him but the feeling gets
stronger the longer I look at him. He shouts at Svetlana
to bring me a pint of 'something long and brown and
English and I don't mean Lenny Henry', and he offers me
the cigar.

'Can't smoke in 'ere,' Svetlana says, pointing to
a sign the Department of Spoil-sports have put up,
slopping my pint on the table.

Trubshawe picks up a battered brown leatherette
briefcase that must have been made before Rover went
bust and we go outside where the 'courtesy' heater is
roaring away like the afterburners of an F-15 Eagle. He
takes a handful of 'literature' from the briefcase and
passes me a leaflet, badly printed, with a picture of an
old MTB superimposed over the Cross of St George on the
front.

This is not Lenny Henry

It reminds me of a film I saw about the Canadian army raid on Dieppe.

That didn't go so well now, did it?

Canadians! They even smell neutral, don't they? Like the wind, or Vicks chest rub, only without the prepubescent sexual connotations.

'Saw what you said about Scotland in the *Sun* the other day,' Trubshawe is saying. 'Thought: that's our man.'

'Our man for what?' I ask.

'The Mother of Parliaments.'

I swear a tear comes into his eye as he says this.

The upshot of this exchange is that he drinks eight pints of bitter while delivering a stirring call to arms - against Scotland.

'If Scotland's so bloody wonderful,' Trubshawe is saying, 'then why in the blue bloody blazes are they all down here, cadging drinks off us and sleeping in tunnels under piss-soaked cardboard?'

'Those are only the successful ones,' I point out.

'Yes,' agrees my new best friend. 'After a childhood spent eating soggy chips - paid for with English money, I'll have you know - they head south, leaving their greasy old

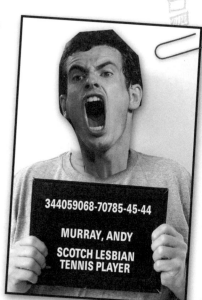

344059068-70785-45-44

MURRAY, ANDY
SCOTCH LESBIAN
TENNIS PLAYER

kilts at the border, and because they're Scotch we give him a chance, don't we? We remember Culloden - '

'With some pleasure!' I interject.

'And we let them get away with it. We let them become MPs and lend clansmen our money, or we let them edit newspapers, or manage football teams. Or if they're women, we let them become continuity announcers on Radio Four.'

Anyway, after a few more pints his meaning came out. The English Democratic Forum wants me to stand for Parliament, on a Get-Rid-of-Scotland platform, at the next general election.

I tell him I'll think about it. He shakes my hand again and peers up at me with those weirdly familiar poached egg eyes.

'Don't leave it too long,' he says, and with that he drives off stinking of drink in a rented Honda Accord.

Where have I seen him before?

WEDNESDAY 17TH MARCH

St Patrick's Day - or St Paddy's Day as we have now to call it to show how inclusive we are - and there is the usual government-sponsored march through Chipping Norton by half a dozen bloodless gingers, followed by the now traditional apology from Bishop Seamus O'Shaughnessy to all the children who were abused by priests in the Catholic Church back in the 1970.

What is it with the Irish and this sort of thing?

I have a theory it is because all the girls have faces like potatoes but there must be something more to it than that, because all the boys do too.

Mind you, I like potatoes.

TUESDAY 23RD MARCH

James still not back from Asia, but we start filming
'We Can Settle Everything in the Whole Wide World by
Having Two Stars Race around the Track in Two
Reasonably Priced Cars'. The King of all China
is too busy to set aside two days, so he'll
come for the race tomorrow, which gives the
Dalai Lama a day's start on getting to grips
with the car and the track.

When he arrives at the studio in
Surrey he's all smiles and waves and
teeth and sweetie-jar glasses and in his
purple robes his sticky little arms and
legs look as if he's made of bits of Peperami.

He wants our autographs - even Rammond's - and
has photos of himself taken standing between us.
I see the shots later and note that I look like
Rammond's slightly creepy uncle, taking him and
his token ethnic minority friend out of school
for an exeat day.

Anyway, it all goes well for a bit until the Dalai
Lama asks where The Smeg is.

You see, he's a big fan of The Smeg.

We look at one another and try to put him off, but he
is determined so off we go.

The Smeg is in his garage as usual. What he does in
there when not driving is anyone's guess, but we hear the
music before we open the doors. It is the sort of music
that quite literally rips your ears off, bundles them up
in barbed wire and then shoves them back up your backside,
sideways, before pulling them back out and slapping them
on the side of your head again. Twice.

Sounds rather good!

37

When we pull back the articulated doors, the floor is covered with glistening porn ripped from cattle-feed magazines, fast food cartons, shoes, party kegs of Watney's Red Barrel left over from the 1970s and God knows what else. Whenever I go in there I am always surprised not to see the skins of human children pegged out on the breezeblock walls.

Anyway, it is colder in than out and the whole place smells of fish oil and emollient and The Smeg is standing in the middle of the room naked except for his white helmet and that weird home-made thong of his, made of twisted bits of leather. His wiry little body is blue with tattoo ink and he is slapping his nipples with the back of a hairbrush.

'Good weekend?' I ask, shouting above the noise.

There is no answer. He just goes on beating himself.

They were never ever exactly going to get along, but the Lama and The Smeg's relationship goes from bad to worse when it turns out that not only can the Lama not drive, he has never been behind the wheel of a car, AT ALL. EVER. NEVER.

Even through The Smeg's helmet visor I can see his face collapse in disbelief.

But worse is to come. As we're taking in that bombshell the Lama reveals he is - officially - a Buddhist!

Yes, ladies and gentlemen, a Buddhist.

We have never knowingly had a Buddhist on *BottomGear* before, except the butch one of Trinny and Susannah but she doesn't count because she's a Liberal Democrat and therefore not to be taken at all seriously.

And if you thought that was bad, he then tells us that not only is he a Buddhist, he is also - wait for it - a vegetablist!

Yes, ladies and gentlemen, the first of our new stars is a practising VEGETABLIST Buddhist!

Amil is panicking, of course, and not just because Natasha has ordered a bucketload of goat curry to be delivered from that Indian place in Godalming and who on earth is going to pay for that? He's panicking more because he thinks he may have ceded Tibet to the Chinese unfairly, since the Lama is at such a disadvantage not being able to drive. I don't point out that being a vegetablist he probably doesn't even have the strength to change gear.

You see that is the problem with vegetablists.

I dare say they are right about some things. I mean, if I were a sheep I probably wouldn't want any old Tom, Dick or Harriet to carry off my children and eat them with boiled potatoes on a Sunday, or slice them up and put them on a long rotating spit and sell bits of them wrapped in bread to drunks, but here's the thing: I am not a sheep.

I may look like one from certain angles and it is true that I am prey as any man to what the Australians so ///
charmingly call dags, but I am irrefutably not a sheep.

So my point is this: what is a vegetablist going to do about it?

He's not going to fight you, is he?

39

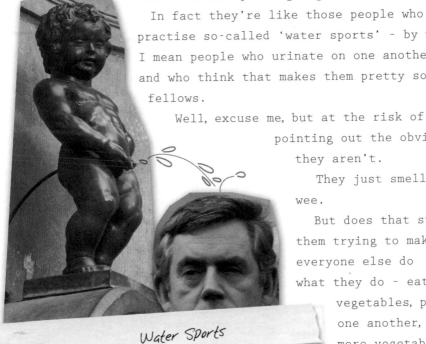

Water Sports

He's certainly not going to bite you.

In fact they're like those people who practise so-called 'water sports' - by which I mean people who urinate on one another - and who think that makes them pretty sound fellows.

Well, excuse me, but at the risk of pointing out the obvious, they aren't.

They just smell of wee.

But does that stop them trying to make everyone else do what they do - eat vegetables, pee on one another, eat more vegetables?

No.

'Fuck!' Amil cries, twitching like an epileptic in a bath, 'what shall we do?'

It is Rammond - RAMMOND! - of all people who comes up with the solution. It has to be something to do with the Zombie voodoo necklace, I know it, but he says that on his way in he passed a funfair in Godalming that had bumper cars. We look at him blankly.

'So what?' Amil asks.

'Well, surely,' he says, 'can't we get His Lamaness to drive one of them? I mean how hard can it be? There's one pedal and a steering wheel.'

And an eerie smile comes over Amil's face.

WEDNESDAY 24TH MARCH

Like rimming six-foot West Indian gentlemen, something
I have always tried to avoid is visiting Godalming. In
fact I've come up with a strapline for the Godalming
tourist board - if such an organization exists - which
they can have for free. It goes something like this:
Godalming: I'd rather have Ann Widdecombe blow a cup of
cold Nitromors up my backside.

Needs a little work, I agree, but there you go.

Anyway, Godalming is where Rammond's funfair is, so go
there we must.

When we get to the fair Amil gets into negotiations
with the one-eyed carney in the dodgems booth - a dead
spit for Ian McShane in his *Lovejoy* days - while his
inbred halfwit son rubs himself against a pole on the
back of one of the dodgem cars as he stares at Natasha's
breasts, today encased in grey cashmere.

Then we wait while the most enormous helicopter comes
down in a field nearby. It's safe to assume that this is
the King of All China because on the helicopter's side
is a big red star denoting something vaguely Chinese.

What is it about stars and military dictatorships?
Show me a country with a star somewhere on its flag and I'll
show you a country whose populace is either a) cartoonishly
fat (Americans), or b) inconsiderate of human
rights (the Chinese, Russians, and basically

WELCOME TO GODALMING

Twinned with Rimming (Baden-Württemberg)

any communist country, including all those dodgy
Middle Eastern countries), or c) incredibly annoying
(Australians and people from New Zealand), or d) a
mixture of a) b) and c) (Americans, again).

   Anyway, out of the helicopter jump a hundred soldiers
of the People's Liberation Army and, seeing them, the
Lama starts, as if he's been caught with his hands down
a panda's pants.

   In fact if he were a car, he'd be - well - a worried-
looking one. A Honda Civic in a minefield perhaps.

   A ramp comes down from the helicopter and it looks
as if the King of All China is going to arrive by tank,
because something the size of the Beijing Gourmet in
Chipping Norton comes rolling out. In fact the Chinese
tank turns out to be a car, though it looks just as
solid as the well-known Chinese restaurant. It is a
sleek black behemoth that looks slightly like a Rolls
Royce if you looked at it in one of those wobbly circus
mirrors.

A Civic in a minefield

Natasha tells me that it is actually a Hongqi V12,
developed by the Chinese car maker FAW, which doesn't
stand for anything as far as I can tell but is in
fact just the company's name. Sadly I don't know the
slightest thing about this new car but from out of it
emerges the Unparalleled King of All China - who looks
just as you would imagine him to except, if this is
possible, even MORE inscrutable - and he certainly isn't
going to let me have a look under the bonnet.

Amil finishes his negotiations and passes Lovejoy a
cheque through the hatch. Lovejoy sniffs it, 'as you
do', and in return gives him a huge bag of green plastic
tokens.

While the backstage monkeys get to work on the dodgems
course (which we've made up as a miniature of the track
at the studio; all the old favourites are there - Gabon,
Hammersmith, gimcrack - and we've even got a stack of
tyres for the cars to bounce against), it is up to me
to tell the Lama and Hu Jintao the rules of the game.
I suddenly feel as if I've stepped back in time to our
colonial past, and here I am come from the West to teach
these Orientals how to do things properly. Each of them
sits on the step to the ring, nodding and murmuring as
their translators whisper poison in their ears, and I
think they rather like being told what to do by a firm
but friendly white man.

It makes them feel safe. It makes them feel cared for.
Something about the proper order of things.

Do you see what I am getting at here?

Well, we can talk about re-colonization later.

In the meantime: 'The rules are very simple,' I tell
them. 'Contestants have to go around the course about

five times, and each of you has to hold a goldfish bowl
here in one hand while you do it. Points will be
awarded for whoever comes first, of course,
but there will be a bonus for whoever
comes in with enough water in their bowl
to keep the goldfish alive.'
They nod.
'Oh, and you have to do it naked.'
This last bit is a joke, but why not? Forbidden by the
Taste and Decency Tsar of the Eurocratic Union, I bet.

Hu Jintao rejects the first car he is given - the seat
torn, some residual squeak on the accelerator caused
by a frayed footwell mat - but takes the next, a chrome
blue beauty with suggestively swirling decals along each
fender. Once he's in and happy, I pass him his goldfish
bowl. As he takes it, I have a strong sense that the
Lama will win.

Not because the Tibetan possesses the greater driving
acumen, no - don't forget the numpty can't drive at all
- but because the King of All China has very very tiny
hands. Each one is no bigger than a postage stamp and
he can scarcely keep a grip on the wheel, let alone the
bowl. I wonder how he signs all those death warrants for
human rightists in China.

With that done, we line them up, the Lama slightly
ahead of the King on account of him taking the first lap
on the inside, and they sit there gripping their wheels
and glaring at one another through their sweetie-jar
glasses.

'Gentlemen,' I say, 'take up your goldfish bowls and
start your engines.'

And with that they're off.

Or rather, they aren't.

Amil has forgotten to hand Lovejoy's halfwit son the tokens, and so Natasha scuttles across and presses two of the little green discs into his wank-paddle and then and only then are the dodgems finally off.

And what an off it is.

Or isn't.

They wheeze around the ring like asthmatic mice.

They are barely moving, and the only thing we can hear over the booming strain of some horrific rub'n'tug music as enjoyed by the young, is them lisping hatred at one another.

Ouch! 'I am going to fuck all Tibet up the bum!' cries the King.

'No you are not,' retorts the Lama. 'We are going to get a Tesco Metro and Polly Toynbee's going to come and live in the Imperial Palace, so fuck you right back!'

HIS LAMANESS

THE KING OF ALL CHINA

45

It's all great fun.

Around and around they go, grinning like maniacs, sweating as if they're melting, their faces as red as Tokyo salarymen after five minutes on the scotch staring at Western hookers in their underwear.

But then we start to notice something funny, something funny that if we are to be honest with ourselves, we should perhaps have foreseen. You see whenever you gather more than two Chinese people in one room they'll strip down to their vests and start gambling. It's what they are like. There is no point complaining. It could be on the result of a game of their so-called Mao's Dong or it could be over the fate of a dodgem car race, or more famously but perhaps inaccurately, a game of Russian roulette.

Anyway, gamble is what the soldiers of the People's Liberation Army do.

They strip off to their white cotton singlets and start to place bets on the race. Pretty soon it's clear most money is going on the Lama. Great bundles of currency are swapping hands and here's another thing about China: the currency.

What is it called?

The rambutan? Something like that.

For such a supposed major player in the world economy, having a low-grade tropical fruit for money is a mistake. Not even the Italians will take you seriously, and they used to have a currency named after a lewd sex act.

Or something.

Anyway, back on the track the Lama is in the lead, and now that he has it, he never looks like losing it. All the King of China can do is huff and puff, but it looks as if he has chosen a marginally slower dodgem. He tries but he just can't catch the little Buddhist, and as they come around Hammersmith for the fifth and final time it looks as if all Tibet is celebrating now.

But then it all goes rather wrong.

You see, one of the Chinese boys - presumably one who had placed his entire family and their pet chickens on the King of all China winning - lets a live cockerel onto the track.

And this is where the Lama's Buddhist vegetablist credentials let him down.

He can't run the thing over. He can't kill an animal.

The cockerel stops in front of him and stares at him, clucking softly, as the Lama stops and stares right back. For a moment he looks like that cowardly tankdriver in Tiananmen Square when faced by the chap with his shopping bags.

Hu Jintao creeps past on the outside, shouting something incomprehensible about paper tigers and running dogs, and he streaks over the line.

So there you have it: Hu Jintao wins, the People's Liberation Army fire their guns in the air and all eight remaining Tibetans are sold into slavery.

And all because of a cock.

After the race we pack up and watch as the Lama hands the keys to Tibet over to the King and climbs wearily into the boot of the Hongqi V12 and away they go.

Rammond has the decency to look a bit sorrowful, but the first of our races is over and we've already solved one of the world's most pressing problems. Next Wednesday it is Benjamin Netanyahooligan versus Khaled 'Mighty' Mashal of Hamas.

FRIDAY 2ND APRIL

Good Friday. I'll warrant Judas was a vegetablist.

SUNDAY 4TH APRIL

Zafira shakes me awake again.

'Jeremy! Jeremy! Wake up! You are having a bad dream!'

I am covered in sweat and for a moment I don't know where I am.

'Was it the same dream again?' she asks.

I nod.

It is a recurring nightmare. I am invited on some panel show and in front of a huge audience I am asked who the best James Bond is. I never know what to say. If I say Roger Moore the audience laugh. If I say Sean Connery the audience groan. If I say Daniel Craig I hear the audience start to leave. If I say George Lazenby there is total silence. If I say Pierce Brosnan the studio lights come up to reveal I am naked, and if I say Timothy Dalton the audience come at me with lighted torches and pitchforks.

It is while I am having a crap and listening to the news about the Chinese occupation of Tibet that it strikes me: if we solved that by having a race, why can't you solve the Bond question that way?

I ring Amil and tell him to get on to it.

'But they won't race against each other,' Amil says. 'Connery won't do anything unless it's for a million pounds, and Moore has gone to ground somewhere in Switzerland.'

'Just ask the girlchild to get on to it, will you? You never know.'

TUESDAY 6TH APRIL

James Might has been arrested!

About time too, of course, but astonishingly it isn't for sex offences.

Some idiot from a news agency rings me first thing this morning to say that he's been caught smuggling a bloody 'conflict' dinosaur egg out of Turkey and have I seen the footage yet? I told them he was a silly bastard and that it could not possibly be true because James is supposed to be smuggling the egg from Sri Lanka.

Free-range dinosaur eggs

I don't tell him, of course, that half of them were mine.

You see, I knew it would all go wrong, but James kept on about it. He kept going on and on about how we could make a killing from these eggs and that maybe if we did that, then we might not have to go on a challenge with Rammond next year...

He said we could 'do our own thing'.

It was just too good a chance to miss.

And in the end I gave in and agreed to go halves on the egg. I wired him the money and got a text back to say he was on his way with the package (packed in Vaseline and stuffed into an extra strong condom) up what we called his 'jxc'.

And then the trouble started.

You see, James made the elementary mistake of flying in an Airbus.

An Airbus.

What does Airbus say to you? The Air bit, yes, that makes sense. Aeroplane has the word in it, albeit spelt differently, so that is all right, but what about the bus bit? The last time I went on a bus I was sat on by an eighteen-stone lesbian from Finchley and ended up in casualty.

←18-STONE LESBIANIST

Anyway, James's Airomnibus inevitably broke down and had to be diverted to Istanbul. Here the Godzilla-like stewardess announced there would be at least an eight-hour delay, but they weren't to worry, because they could all go and pass the time in the delightful first-class transfer lounge.

Well thank you very much, Istanbul airport. I'd rather try urinating a wing nut.

I mean, have you ever BEEN to Istanbul?

To call it a toilet is an insult to Greece.

Anyway, it was in the toilet of this toilet that James made his fateful error. And he made it because, James being James, he ate some of the 'complimentary snacks' on offer. He even drank some of the 'free' water, too.

Now these complimentary snacks had been on the plate so long they predated the Crusades, and the water was so old there were still pieces of the ark floating in it.

Not surprisingly, then, after James had eaten the biscuits and drunk the water, alarm bells began ringing.

You see, that's the thing about foreign food: IT MAKES YOU ILL.   ✓✓✓Ask Keith Floyd!!!

So James went to the bog and it was a sign of his desperation, ladies and gentlemen, that he actually undid his trousers and squatted down on a toilet. A Turkish toilet, may I remind you.

James takes another shit

Whereupon he promptly managed to crap the dinosaur egg out at such a force the loaded condom shot around the U-bend and vanished up - or down - the pipe.

Now this egg was worth a mint, of course, so even feeling as ill as he was, James took off his shirt, and plunged his arm down into the toilet bowl.

Where it promptly got stuck.

Yes, ladies and gentlemen, James Might was stuck in the lavatory.

He would have been there from Monday to Saturday perhaps, because no one - not one solitary soul - came past until late that night when a security guard was doing his rounds (or, as it is known in Turkey, looking for somewhere to kip, or to plant a bomb, one or the other) and caught James with his trousers down - literally - and his arm rammed down the toilet.

In most other countries you suppose the guard would have taken steps to help him out, but this being Turkey, the guard whipped out his mobile phone and took a three-minute film which shows James in what you might not call a positive light.

Then, instead of calling the duty plumber and freeing James, the security guard called the Turkish equivalent of Max Clifford, and now the film is all over the

Death of a Princess

interwebby thing and the security guard can afford his
own shop to sell pointy slippers, kebabs and venereal
disease to passing tourists.

At lunchtime I turn the news on and there, you've
guessed it, is Rammond - RAMMOND! - whose hair was even
stranger than ever, trying to look innocent and saying
there is probably a perfectly reasonable explanation and
that this sort of thing happens to anyone and that it
is perfectly fine to stick your hand down the toilet of a
first-class transfer lounge and that James had probably
just dropped something down there, 'as you do'.

The next moment the programme cuts to a large bald-
headed man with a moustache like a small German dog,
wearing a fancy-dress shop military uniform shouting
at the screen and waggling a dirty great finger at the
camera. He is the Turkish plenipotentiary - or something
- to the Court of St James, and he is very unhappy that
we should be sending agents into his country to unsettle
and destabilize what - apparently - is already a tense
situation.

And then comes the worst news of all.

The Turks suspect James Might of being - wait for it
- in the Special Air Service. The SAS.

I turn the telly off.

I mean, am I missing something here?

The closest James has been to the SAS is playing
Call of Duty: Modern Warfare on PlayStation when we
have our boys' nights in, so the thought of him in the
SAS is biblically absurd, although, thanks to the recent
cutbacks in our armed forces, it wouldn't completely
surprise me if he was at least working undercover for
the CCF, by which I mean the Combined Cadet Force.

But what about me? I look at myself in the mirror. Time and tide and the odd carvery dinner have eased my rugged good looks, that is fair to say, but despite what Amil and the others say about my face looking like a 'warm ball sack', isn't there something somewhere in that middle-distance gaze I have, something that gives just a hint of the sort of impulse that drove T. E. Lawrence?

Not his penchant for young boys with dusky skin, of course, but a sense of bigger things? Grander schemes?

MONDAY 12TH APRIL

The Prime Minister calls the election. July the 29th. Thank God we won't have to see his ugly Cyclops Scotch mug on our boxes for very much longer. No sooner does he thank us and wish us well than Major Ron Trubshawe (Ret'd) is on the line again, ringing from a call box in his office in the Membury/Swindon motorway services. He wonders if I've had time to read his 'guff'. Tell him I'm still thinking about his offer.

'Don't leave it too long,' Trubshawe says, and then his money runs out.

Can I really stand for parliament, though? What if the truth about that night in Germany gets out? What would I say then? That it was just a joke and you shouldn't listen to a silly balding fat bloke with a dodgy hip and a face like an old oiled scrotum? I don't think that'd work in this case.

Worse is to come, though, when the chairman of the local Tories drops by for his long promised 'chat' and is driving a Rover 75. I almost don't answer the door.

'What do you want?' I shout through the fan window.

He introduces himself. Alan Something.

I open the door, but don't let him in. He surveys the garage.

'Lovely spread you've got yourself here, Jez. Admire a man what's done himself proud.'

He's wearing a bright grey suit, slightly shiny, and underneath is a round-neck knitted pullover. On his feet his shoes look like Cornish pasties. If he were a car, well, he'd be a Rover 75.

I ask him why he's here.

'Read your piece on Bolivia,' he says. 'Loved it. Loved the way you rhymed Bolivia with Chlamydia, to the detriment of Chlamydia.'

That was Zafira's joke, but I no breath would pickle an egg at thousand paces and the sides of his head are shaved and he is trembling like an uncle at his niece's netball final. *A cracker!!* Turns out he also wants me to stand in the forthcoming general election, for the Tories, in the local constituency. I tell him I'm not very popular with the locals ever since I bought the local disused RAF airfield and let The Smeg live there. Just then: a brainwave.

'HILARIOUS'
RHYMES TO STIR THINGS UP

Bolivia — chlamydia
Micronesia — schizophrenia
Nicaragua — second-hand Jaguar
Nigeria — urticaria
North Korea — gonorrhoea
South Korea — diarrhoea
Zafira xxx

'I'll do it,' I say, 'if you can get James Might out of jail.'

He laughs glumly and then says something about being tough on crime and tough on the causes of crime.

I don't say anything.

'Can I come in, then?' he asks.

'No,' I say.

'Jez,' he says. 'Jez, Jez, Jez Jez Jez. The Jezster. The Jizm-meister.'

It starts to rain, spitting really.

I wonder if he's crying.

'I'll push off now then,' he says.

'I think that's best,' I agree.

He passes me a leaflet. A picture of David Cameron looking interested in your concerns. His face is as blank as a beach ball.

The Man from UKIP

He has at best three months before the election to spring James, but I am not hopeful.

Later that afternoon the strange-sounding man from UKIP comes up the drive in a van. I think he might be coming to mend the boiler or something and come out to greet him. He gets out looking like a failed banker, in a blazer, with a fleshy silk tie and a stripy shirt. His head is as sleek as a weasel's in a pool of olive oil.

Turns out he wants me to stand for UKIP in the next elections too.

I tell him about James in prison. That has become my test of political parties now. Forget education, forget the economy, forget all the hospices and so on. Will they get James out?

'You'll have to get out and start knocking on doors,' he says, ignoring my James Might test.

'But I haven't said I will.'

'Oh you will,' he says and I suddenly feel a chill down my spine. Who is this little man?

'Did I tell you I know the councillor with the overview of local traffic control?' he says.

'No.'

'Well, I do. In fact she's in my pocket.'

I can't help glancing at his pocket.

'She decides where all the sleeping policemen go. Where to put the speed bumps and so on.'

'Really?' I say.

'How would you like a speed bump at the bottom of your drive?'

For a moment I am lost for words. He smiles at me as if he has just sold snake oil to a blind man.

'You're threatening me with a speed bump?'

'Not threatening. Inviting you to consider the possibility of having one installed. I can also sell you solar panelling, too, if you are interested? And a wind turbine?'

He hands me some leaflets, one for UKIP, with a photo of him sneering at the camera like someone with a cashback mini ISA, and two for his solar heating installation company.

I watch him go, wondering what on earth UKIP even stands for.

Inside, Zafira is working on my column: Why I hate hotdogs.

Next to her on the desk is the stuff from Ron Trubshawe and I have the leaflets from the Tories and UKIP in my hand. I hold them out. The financial advisor, the MTB, David Cameron. Which is worse? Not sure. I pin them to the side of the fridge with magnets and try to arrange them in order of coolness.

Which is it to be?

For the moment it isn't a contest.

It has to be the MTB.

I ring Trubshawe's office.

'Hello Coffee Primo? Svetlana speaking how may I help you?'

I let out a long plume of breath.

For my maiden speech in Parliament!!! ////

Entering politics for the first time is a great moment, like leaping into a hot tub of warm champagne with the girls from IcelandAir, all of them naked except their hats and at least two of them yieldingly comatose.

FRIDAY 23RD APRIL

I drive up to London in the Range Rover again for another one of Amil's gender-knitting-awareness-workshops. Last week we solved the Middle Eastern Question thanks to some very nippy driving by the Arab fellow from Hamas - used to driving getaway

cars, I suppose - and the Israeli state has since pulled
back to within the old 1948 borders.

Now that the Occupied Territories aren't occupied any
more, you'd have thought the Turks would have been happy,
wouldn't you? What with pan-Arabic brotherhood and so
on. You'd even think they might give us James Might in
return, but no, not a bit of it.

He's waiting for his trial in a police station,
playing cards with beefy shaven-headed policemen. At
stake: his anal virginity.

I slide my compilation CD into the stereo and up comes
one of my all-time favourite driving songs, 'Radar Love',
by Golden Earache. Sensational driving song, one of the
best ever written in any language and once again I can't
stop myself singing along.

'I've been drivin' all night, my hand's wet on the
wheel, there's a voice in my head that drives my heel,
It's my baby callin', says I need you here, and it's half
past four and I'm shitting a pear.'

I am in my Chevvy again. I'm rolling along the freeway
with my shirt off and a roll of toilet paper in the
glove compartment and the wind in my hair...

And THAT'S when the idea hits me.

Now I know that a lot of what we do on *BottomGear* is
childish and irresponsible, and that we have particular
anal fixations, but as you can see, we have turned over a
new leaf, haven't we? We've brought peace (well, China,
really) to Tibet and souvenir shops to the so-called
occupied territories, and next week we're giving Gerry
Adams a go against Ian Paisley to decide the fate of
Northern Ireland, but there is a wrong to be righted that
is much closer to home.

That's right.

James Might.

So my idea is this: we DRIVE to Turkey to save James Might OURSELVES.

We'll make it this year's *BottomGear* Christmas Special!

As soon as I see what a good idea this is I am pounding on the horn. I am hooting with mirth. I am bellowing along with Golden Earache,

'When he's lonely and the longing gets too much, he sends a cable comin' in from above...'

It has to be one of the most epically brilliant songs ever recorded. You see, although there are a lot of songs out there that are about love and wet hands on the steering wheel, what sets 'Radar Love' apart, what makes it a TRULY brilliant song, what makes it the Lamborghini Murciélago LP640 of driving songs, is that simple image of a 'cable coming in from above'.

Now Rammond says that line reminds him of the phrase 'laying a cable' - one of his euphemisms for taking a crap - but for me, it is the distilled essence of

Typical Dutch Scene

THE BOY WITH HIS FINGER IN THE DYKE

driving. Just as Brigitte Bardot (before she turned twenty and mad from eating too many vegetables) was the essence of womanhood, so this image captures the experience of driving. It makes me think of driving anywhere - to Knebworth, say, on an overcast Thursday afternoon through static traffic, or through the night, on my way to Bumfucky, Tennessee, alone, bare-chested, sweating, country music on the radio, my ball-bag face lit up by the soft glow of the dials.

A shame, then, that Golden Earache is a Dutch band.

What else have the Dutch given the world, I wonder, apart from Edam cheese, elm disease and a place to go to be legally fellated on the street while you're off your mind on mushrooms? Not much.

You see, here's the thing about Holland: you can't see it from the sea.

Nowhere should be like that, not even Chad, and you can hardly see Chad from space. Or rather, you can, but there is nothing to be seen. If you think the Dutch were miserly when it came to sharing their gifts with the world, wait until you see Chad. What have they given us? Sand? Scrub? Acacia?

Thanks guys! You must come again.

I am wealthier than Chad. And Iceland, as it turns out, and now Greece and Ireland, Spain, Portugal and Italy.

Why? Because I -

Because I come up with ideas to save people from Turkish prisons.

WEDNESDAY 28TH APRIL

Ordinarily I'd rather share a lazy afternoon and a jar of rohypnol with Jeffrey Dahmer than go to the cinema,

Up yours, François Truffaut!!

but today's Zafira's birthday, so off we go to see the latest offering from Hollywood-land.

Now I like Hollywood films - the hyperrealism of the motorboat chases, the abundance of Nazi gold, the possibility of a flash of Dame Keira's knickers - but of course Zafira doesn't like that sort of film and so instead we watch - if watch is the word you use to describe sitting in the dark holding your breath and pressing your thumbs so hard into your eye-sockets that you actually push your eyeballs into your scrotum - a film about lactose-intolerant middle-aged women coming to terms with their wasted lives.

Joanna Lumley (who you would've, wouldn't you, back in her *New Avengers* days, and I bet a million Gurkhas still would), Isabella Rossellini (ditto, though maybe not the Gurkhas) and Jessica Lange (not after all that plastic surgery) star in a Camel Toe Productions film of *The Wizard's Sleeve*, produced by the same team that bored you to death last time you tried to watch anything that didn't star Clint Eastwood.

THE WORST FILMS EVER: THE SHORTLIST

1. Anything French

2. Anything German

3. Anything Russian

4. Anything by Ingmar Bergman

5. Calendar Girls (I've never been so grateful for the six-inch virgin screen)

6. Brickbat Mountain

At the end there is so much weeping from so many post-hormonal women that I am surprised I do not come away pregnant.

✓✓✓
Should go down a storm on the Review Show!!!

Worse is to come though, because on the way home Zafira tells me she has agreed that I will front an advertising campaign for a company called HomeGrown™.

'What does HomeGrown™ make?' I ask.

She tells me. HomeGrown™ make a substance that you rub on your bald patch to make your hair grow again.

'Why would they want me to front their campaign?' I ask.

Zafira is uncharacteristically quiet.

'Jeremy - ' she starts, but I cut her off.

'I'm not bald, you know.'

Her reply is lost because just as we turn into the drive, I catch a badger in my headlights and run the thing down.

Zafira screams.

I stay icy calm.

Did I mention that I have recently taken up the post of president of the British Bull-Bar Association?

Homegrown candidate

Anyway, the badger is, as you might imagine, completely dead. Its eyeball is broken and some grey porridge has leaked from a rather nasty-looking graze on the top of its head.

Here's what no one will tell you about badgers: they are the most epically stupid animals ever invented. They make killer whales look intelligent, and it is

✓✓✓
UP Yours Attenborough!

no coincidence that they have the same colouring. Black
and white. It is nature's way of saying: back off, I am
dangerously stupid. Just look at Alistair Darling.

More than that, some of them are, actually, gay.

So what am I going to do with a dead, gay, badger at
the bottom of my drive?

A Gay badger

That's right.
I'm going to blow
it up.

Now, thanks to
the Department of
Fretting Needlessly,
it is illegal to buy
ammonium nitrate in
industrial quantities
without a so-called
licence but happily
I have one or two
sacks stored in the
garage 'against
eventuality'. With
the addition of
some diesel and
an old-fashioned
match of the
Bryant and May
variety, I soon have the makings of a bomb so large it
would make Guido Fawkes come in his pants.

I pack the sacks around the badger's body, cover them
with old tractor tyres and pour a gallon or so of diesel
over the pyre and stand back a bit.

Then I strike the match.

The explosion is biblical.

I wake up a little later, lying naked in a field with a paramedic asking me to count up to five.

'He's never been able to do that,' I hear Zafira saying over his shoulder.

I deliberately count up to six.

'Should be all right,' the paramedic says, 'but keep him away from the whisky.'

He packs his things into the back of the ambulance.

It is as we walk around the crater and back up to the house that Zafira starts to laugh. When she opens the door and guides me to a mirror, I begin to see why.

You see, not only am I naked, I am also a) completely black (which explains why the dog starts barking when he sees me) and b) completely bald.

Zafira is already dialling HomeGrown™ to increase my fee.

MONDAY 3RD MAY

Samantha Cameron. You would, wouldn't you?

I am thinking this as I pass a sign to Notting Hill and I am stuck behind one Fiat Multipla trying to overtake another Fiat Multipla while going up a slight incline.

Some people say that what a car looks like matters less than how it works, but excuse me, bollocks to that.

Yes it has to work, but there is no excuse for this sort of car.

Fiat Multiplas are so epically ugly that seeing two of them together is like catching your parents experimenting with the sixty-nine position.

√√√ must use on BottomGear!!

Not something you ever want to see again.

Yeeüürrrghhh!

Except to chase some ramblers off my fields at home, this is the first time I've been out of the house since the explosion, and when I get to the BBC the girlchild is, for once, like, lost for words? I am wearing a hat Zafira has bought me to cover my pate, but my emperor penguin's eyebrows are gone, as are the tufts of cotton wool I like to keep in my ears, and I am aware that without them I look even more than usual like an oiled scrotum.

Now that I finally get the chance to put my idea of saving James to Amil, he says no.

'This is about health and safety, isn't it?' I shout. 'You don't want us to go down to Istanbul and free our friend, because you're afraid we might get scratched and sue the BBC!'

Rammond sits in the corner. He's got his chair turned around, brand-new haircut, same old mad stare. He breaks the news that James has already been tried and sentenced to life in Sagmalcilar prison, the one made famous by the film *Midnight Express*.

'No one's ever come out of there alive!' Amil wails.

'Then we must do it.'

'How?'

'Beetles!' Rammond says. 'We drive there in second-hand Beetles we can't pay more than £500 for on eBay and we offer the guards anything they like if they'll let him go.'

I am not having that.

'Beetles? The worst car in the world ever? The same Beetles that prevented Hitler reaching Moscow?'

There is some consternation at this point. Amil says I've got the wrong end of the stick, but if the Beetles had been better made, then the Wehrmacht would have made it to Moscow, beaten the Russians, and we would never have had the Trabant or the Lada. So.

'No,' I say. 'We want something grander than that.'

Again I feel the blood of T. E. Lawrence flowing in my veins.

'Such as what?' Natasha asks. She is in camel-coloured cashmere today and she has a visible bra strap line.

'A tank,' I say, 'each.'

'Too slow!'

'A helicopter?'

'It's a car show.'

'What about those Snatch Land Rovers the army use in Afghanistan? We could get hold of one of them.'

'Too dangerous,' Amil says.

And I tell them that I am not driving in anything named after a woman's front bottom. Front bottom is on Zafira's 'Must Mention' list.

'Front bottom!' Rammond gasps, as you do. We all look at Natasha as the only woman in the room and for a moment, none of us know what the others are thinking, but I am trying to guess what colour underwear she is wearing.

'Pink,' I say, aloud.

Suddenly I am sure everybody knows at least what I have been thinking.

'Pink?' Amil mumbles, he starts blushing. 'Pink what? Pink cars?'

'Exactly!'

'Just cars that are pink? Doesn't seem very special.'

'No! Not just cars that are pink. Pink Panthers.'

'Pink Panther's car? The one he arrives in at the beginning of the cartoon?'

This is from Rammond and it is an idea that briefly trips me up. What sort of car was that I wonder?

Amazingly Natasha knows what I mean even if Rammond doesn't.

'Pink Panther,' she tells us, 'was the nickname soldiers gave the Land Rover 72 Series IIa 109, officially known as Truck, General Service, 3/4 Ton, or FV 18064, which was adapted for the SAS to use in the desert. They painted them pink to match the sand, gave them four fuel tanks so they could carry an extra 100 gallons of petrol, a heavy-duty chassis, springs, sand tyres, guards to the diffs and a specially mounted spare wheel.'

A pink Panther — I've already got a semi!

'What about the guns and so on?' I ask.

'GPMG, anti-tank weapon, rifles, grenade holders, smoke canisters and navigation equipment.'

'Can we get all that?' Amil asks doubtfully.

'Might not be too happy about the hardware on the Channel Tunnel,' Natasha says.

'We'll cross that bridge when we get to it.'

Even though it's a tunnel.

So here's the plan: Rammond and I will each drive one of these Land Rovers down through France to Italy. From there we'll find some sort of boat to take us across the sea to Greece and then we'll drive across into Turkey. What we'll do when we get there is another matter.

Already I have a semi.

SUNDAY 9TH MAY

My birthday. I've been married to Zafira for so long now that the chance of being woken up with a hot-tea blow-job is out of the question, so I wake instead to the sound of dogs barking.

Ramblers.

I roll out of bed and through the window there is Janet Street bloody Porter tramping across the ploughed

fields below. Behind her is a line of terminally sag-
teated feminists with greasy hair and maroon anoraks.

With their hoods and shiny coats they look like a
line of dingy sex-aids marching across the fields on
their way to a vegetablists' céilidh.

I stare at them for a while, trying to work out what
it is that they are supposed to be enjoying.

Is it the fresh air? No. That can't be possible
thanks to the talcum powder and the hot pheromone reek
of the obligatory transsexual harpist from Ebbw Vale
that by law has to be included in every rambling group.

Is it the scenery then?

Nope. Can't be that either. They have to walk in file,
you see, like ships of the line, and each one of them so
broad in the beam that light can't bend around them.

What is the appeal then?

I'll tell you.

Rambling is dogging for the psychotically shy. ✓✓✓ Another
one for
Think about it: they drive to remote car parks   ST
where, instead of performing graphic sexual acts on column!
the bonnets of their infernal Toyota Priuses for the
entertainment of strangers, they snort and tut while
one of them pulls on her lesbian walking boots and the
other checks the thermos lid is screwed tight.

I bet they play Twister when it is raining.

When I get down to breakfast Zafira gives me my
present.

A recipe book.

My face falls further than the stock price of Lehman
Brothers Holdings.

Since when did you give men cookery books for their
birthday?

Zafira is still furious with me for
refusing to front the HomeGrown™
campaign. I do not tell her
that I've found an alternative
advertising campaign to front
and that even now I am in
negotiations with Levi Strauss
to become what they are calling
their global brand ambassador.
I spoke to the CEO who
said his lawyers would be
in touch, but I don't tell
Zafira. I want this to come
as a surprise.

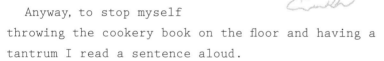

Anyway, to stop myself
throwing the cookery book on the floor and having a
tantrum I read a sentence aloud.

'Cauliflower is something I can live without, but today
it surprises me in a salad...'

If there is one person I blame for the state
of the nation today it is Nigel Bloody Slater.

*Another one
for that maiden
✓✓✓✓ speech in the
House*

Back when Britain was great and we had a car industry
worth talking about, we drank beer for breakfast and
our women were yellow from their work in the munitions
factory. We didn't mess about with cauliflower in salads
or if we did we'd've had the good sense not to mention
it in public.

Now though, here's Nigel hinting darkly at his
domestic set-up and telling us that he likes to cook
with the doors open, even if it's raining.

And we buy it! We go out and spend our hard-earned
cash on that sort of nonsense!

When grown men write openly about cauliflower, then you know it is time to leave the country. ✓✓✓ *Abso-fucking-lutely!!*

No wonder the French are laughing up their sleeves at us.

It is precisely this sort of thing that turned their once great country from the one that produced Gustave Eiffel into the gayest in the world. I mean, think about it. Name ten Frenchmen who've done *anything* in the last fifty years.

1. That Algerian who butted the Italian in the World Cup football final.
2. Raymond Blanc, who moved to England where his accent only got stronger.
3. Jacques Cousteau's son, what's-his-name.
4. Sarkozy, the little chap in the stacked heels, famous for marrying Carla Bruni. (You would, wouldn't you? Just so long as she promised not to get her guitar out afterwards, and that's from me, who loves a ballad.)
5. Jean-Claude Killy.
6. Er, that's it.

The rest of them are either waiters, overpaid nancy football players, or from somewhere else.

TUESDAY 25TH MAY

Take the new Mercedes for a test drive and nearly park it in the back of a supermarket delivery lorry. On the side is a giant picture of that oaf Jamie Oliver, urging us to try something different.

Why?

He is another one I blame for the state of this country.

What he simply doesn't understand about the underclass is that feeding them proper food is a waste of money.

I mean think about it.

It doesn't take a maths genius to see that giving a hoody ten pounds' worth of food a day when he might get by on a 90p bag of chips is a waste of £9.10 if at the end of that day he turns up in hospital to a) get his stomach pumped because he has put so much cider in it, or b) be pronounced dead on arrival because someone has shanked him in the local park.

√√√ *worth mentioning to G. Osborne?*

It doesn't make sense.

And Oliver's scheme to get a restaurant staffed entirely by the feckless poor was doomed from the start. And patronizing too. What if I opened a garage staffed only with lunatics? Or mechanics with Irritable Bowel Syndrome? Or tyre-fitting Tourettists?

I drive on in silence for a moment, listening to the car.

The more I think about this idea, though, the more aroused I get, and the faster I drive.

I hurl the car - this one feels just like any of the others, except more so - around the bends and I imagine a workshop full of panel-beating epileptics. The noise would be sensational and the results would be, well, not perfect, but who could complain? No *Guardian* reader would dare. They would be fair-trade panel beaters!

Perhaps that should be my next big thing?

I could make it into a television show!

I could call it *Jeremy's Garage* and have a ten-part series and I'd start with about ten of them and at the end of each episode I'd call one of them into my office, decked out with calendars of naked girls and bumper

73

stickers and so on, and then I'd fire them. The winner
would get a job at Kwik Fit.

I screech around the corner into the drive and
nothing can stop me, not even the speed bump that
someone has installed while I've been out. It stops
the car dead, true, and there are sparks and a horrible
wrenching noise as the sump comes away, but who cares?

It is, after all, just a car.

FIVE POLITICIANS TO USE AS SPEED BUMPS

Gordon Brown

Peter Mandelson (too thin?)

Diane Abbott (she'd stop an armoured car, at least)

John Prescott (and he'd stop a fucking tank . . .)

Eric Pickles (and he'd stop an entire Panzer division)

WEDNESDAY 2ND JUNE

A letter from Levi Strauss & Co.'s lawyers. Hid it
from Zafira so it'll come as a surprise and
opened it in the bog. They don't want me
to be brand ambassador, it turns out. They
want me to 'cease and desist' from wearing
their jeans on my shows. They are drawing
up an injunction against me approaching
within five yards of any one of their
products.

I am depressed about this for
exactly a minute because then Zafira
my wife-and-manager bangs on the door.

Snugfit

'You're not in there with your finger up your bottom again are you, Jez?' she shouts.

SUNDAY 6TH JUNE

Trubshawe rings. He's glad to have got me on the 'blower' and suggests lunch next week at The Lamb and Foreskin to meet 'the other candidate' and go through the manifesto.

He asks me to jot down my ideas.

My manifesto involves the usual stuff about foreigners and people who aren't like me and don't like exactly what I like yet who seem to be getting their way when they shouldn't. I write out a list of the things that I will, basically, ban: communists, cyclists, lesbian-ramblers, Guardian readers, Labour and Tory voters, vegetablists, ultra-veganists, golfosexualists, wine columnists, anyone with a high-visibility vest, jockeys, pederasts,

679559065-94445-55-60

WOODS, TIGER
GOLFOSEXUALIST

transsexuals, lesbians (again), the Welsh, nancy football players whose children have made-up names, wind-turbines, rotary club members, greasy-haired feminists, Sebastian bloody Faulks, the thousand-year EuroReich, Quentin Willson, hammerhead sharks, potholers and enthusiasts of every stripe, up to and including car bores, Romanians in shawls, polar bear combo acts, privileges for well-behaved prisoners, caravanists, homeless charities that encourage the Scotch to come to London, knitted ties, Lindisfarne, aerobics, The Kingston Trio, Shane Warne, bat-winged jumpers on women over 23 and mini chicken kievs.

These are just some of them.

Outside I notice someone has put a very small car in my drive.

It is clearly Korean and no bigger than a microwave oven, and when I open the door I am surprised it does not open with a ping to reveal a still steaming, cooked dog dinner.

Zafira tells me I must test-drive this sort of thing to show that I am not obsessed with cars beyond the reach of the man in the street.

Pop the terrier in and set the timer for two minutes

I get in, still swearing I can smell roast terrier, and the car sags to one side and my knees are around my ears. It is as if I were committing auto-fellatio, something I haven't managed since I buggered my hip a while back.

But now here's the thing about cheap cars.

They're a dreadful mistake.

They're a dreadful mistake because if you buy one and drive it on a public road, someday soon you will be in a head-on collision with a Range Rover being driven on the wrong side of the road by a pomaded footballer with

a Ukrainian hooker between his legs and half a pound of
Colombia's finest (and only) up his nose.

And what happens to you when that happens?

Yep. You end up dead. And then some.

It is, as the Japanese used to say as they were
strapped into their Zeroes and pointed at the USS
Yorktown, quite simply, *sayonara*.

Not that that seems to figure in people's calculations
when it comes to buying a car, does it?

Oh no.

They go into a garage, see a price, decide that's
what they can afford and then they hand the money over
without ever checking that the car even has a sixth gear
or that its bodywork isn't made from the laminated by-
product of the pizza pie-making industry.

No wonder so many of them die.

Here are the top six cars I'd like to crash into, in
no particular order of preference: the infernal Toyota
Prius (although since their brakes don't work they're
tricky to find in order to crash into), the Twingo, the VW
Up! Lite, any make of smart Car, the
Fiat Multipla (and Panda), the Tata
Nano, anything and everything made
by Seat, Hyundai and/or Daewoo, as
well as the Bentley Flying Spur.

On second thoughts, not the
Bentley. Not because I like it -
I don't - but because it weighs
eleventy trillion tons and you'd
need a thermonuclear device to
knock it over.

The others you'd hardly

SIX CARS I'D LIKE TO
CRASH INTO:
THE SHORTLIST

Toyota Prius

Renault Twingo

VW Up! Lite

Smart Car

Fiat multipla

Tata Nano

notice if you ran them over. It'd be like stepping on a Styrofoam cup, filled with the bones of four unusually small voles.

And here is a list of the top few cars I'd like to be driving when I crash into them: a Hummer, an eighth-hand vintage Silver Shadow, a Mercedes Sprinter loaded with bricks, a Toyota Hi-Lux, a Bentley Flying Spur (again and why not?), a Vulva D40, anything with a bull-bar, a Range Rover.

I have another list of cars that I'd like to land on from above - dropped from a crane, say - and yet another of cars in which I'd like to land on them in, but there is some crossover between the lists, I have to say.

TUESDAY 8TH JUNE

Back up to the BBC again to talk to Amil and Natasha about the *BottomGear* Christmas Special. Amil suggests we pretend we can only find one Pink Panther, so that we have to make one ourselves in the garage at the track. That bit's easy enough, and the viewers love it when we stick something together and it sinks or catches fire or falls over and squashes some old gypsy or something. Then we can mug to camera as if we were in an episode of *The Monkees*.

Then we move on to the Bond-off and, thinking about it, I can already feel something long and pale stirring in my pants.

'About the Bonds in the Reasonably Priced Cars?' the girlchild says, 'there's some good and bad news?'

We wait while these questions go on for five minutes. A rough calculation reveals that every year lesbian schoolteachers cause British industry to lose five trillion working days with all these stupid questions.

Anyway the upshot is that Timothy Dalton will do it if Pierce Brosnan will, and Brosnan will if we fly him first class there and back, and George Lazenby will if we buy him a bull. Daniel Craig will do it if he can choose his own car.

'And, like, Sean Connery will do it for a million pounds?'

'A million fucking quid just to drive a car around?' I can't stop myself barking. 'Is he fucking joking?'

There is a silence for a second or two. Everybody is looking at me.

The girlchild carries on.

'I don't think so? Oh, and he also wants it written into his contract? That he gets to beat Roger Moore?'

'Hmm. Well, I suppose we could do that. And what about Moore?'

'He's gone into hiding? In Switzerland or somewhere? And no one can find him?'

FRIDAY 18TH JUNE
Lunch with Trubshawe at the Foreskin starts badly.

There is a Porsche Panamera parked in my space. It is a perfectly ordinary Porsche ✓✓✓✓ Panamera, in that it is yelp-out-loud ugly, *One for the next* as ugly as Margaret Beckett in a thong, but *show!* whoever owns it had contrived to make it even worse by keeping a panama hat on the parcel shelf.

You don't look at the fireplace while you're poking the fire!

Having a panama hat on the parcel shelf was all right when your dad did it, because he wasn't a child abuser. If YOU do it, well, you are putting out the international symbol that tells the world you are not to be trusted around children. The only thing that is worse is to have a cushion there, and a box of peach-coloured paper tissues.

Trubshawe's at the bar again but this time he's not alone. Standing next to him is the other candidate for the English Nation Defence League and when I see him, my blood seethes audibly in my veins.

It is that poor man's version of me: John Littledick.

His is the horrible Porsche in the car park. His is the horrible hat. I might have guessed.

It transpires we three are the quorum of the English Party for Formal Democracy - or something. It takes me about a second to see we have nothing in common, but out we go and smoke under the heater and glare at one another while coming up with things we will ban.

'Smoking outside,' I say, looking around.

Trubshawe licks the end of his pencil and jots this down in an old exercise book.

'Lesbians,' Littledick says.

'I've already got that down.' I say, 'Twice.'

'Men in spats then,' he tries.

'Don't be so absurd. Coconuts.'

'Coconuts? Hah. Frenchmen.'

Damn, I think, I wish I'd thought of that.

'Avocados.'

'Calling football soccer.'

'Those blue lights that kill flies in cheese shops.'

'*Ace Ventura: Pet Detective.*'

'Marzipan.'

'Any reference, whatsoever, to Luxembourg.'

'Traffic cones,' he says, and I can see he's now just trying to make friends.

'Pelicans.'

'Sleeping with your sister.'

There is a moment's silence.

'I think, John,' Ron says carefully, 'that in some parts of the country that's already frowned on.'

'Linford Christie, then.'

'Sleeping with Linford Christie or just Linford Christie?'

'Both.'

'Agreed.'

'Quilted bog roll.'

'Segways.'

This goes on until Trubshawe runs out of space in his book. Outside it is dark. We are exhausted. We have promised to roll back central government while introducing a raft of new legislation that seems at first glance arbitrary, but is in fact informed by a

No!

horribly misplaced and bristling sense of injustice.

TUESDAY 29TH JUNE

Here's something no one ever tells you about the Television Centre: it is incredibly big. The corridors are so long you could get from 0 to 60 down most them, in a diesel smart Car, and even then towing a trailer packed with illegal immigrants.

Death is too good for them

Or you could do, that is, if the corridors weren't so cluttered with moustachioed women of the baggy-breasted variety, slopping along in bunion sandals to their residential macramé plant-hanger sensitivity workshops.

But I've been thinking about this, in relation to the ramblers, that is, and here's a thought: why don't we bring all those ramblers up here to Television Centre and let them ramble around the place?

They're easy enough to spot in their cagoules and practical trousers and lesbian boots, so why not collect them in depots at major train stations around the country and then ship them up here in cattle trucks? We could take care of any of their valuables - gold teeth, shoes, spectacles, retirement watches - and then pack them through security and just let them wonder around the corridors until they die.

They'd love it - and they might get to see Patrick Kielty as they pass.

It's what Rammond calls a 'win-win' situation.

I mean, think about it.

First, we would be getting them out of the woods, which is a good thing since the only reason they are there in the first place is to find a new vantage point for spying on primary-school playgrounds.

Second, since so many ramblers are of the elderly

persuasion, getting rid of them would halve the pension
burden on the rest of us, so we'd have more cash to spend
on cars and roads. (And we'd also be clearing the roads
of all those tiny irritating plastic cars driven by
people wearing white hair and car coats, unable to see
over the wheel without the use of a tartan incontinence
cushion).

What's more, we could charge their living relatives to
take them off their hands, thereby making a profit and so
be able to scrap the licence fee.

That has got to be good, hasn't it? Or am I missing
something here.

In fact the only people who might have reason to
complain about this are the folks who live on top of the
Swiss hill, by whom I mean Dignitas. They'd be furious at
the thought of all that business withering away in White
City instead of in their own Swiss gas chambers.

But I have a two-part solution for them.

The first bit is to allow them to offer their service
to anyone who wants it, not just the terminally ill, and
the second is to allow them to advertise their services
on telly.

Never mind HomeGrown™, that's one campaign I'd be
happy to front.

I can imagine it going something along the lines of
that advert for 'good old Yellow Pages' back in the
1980s, when J. R. Hartley was after his bloody book on
fly fishing, except that of course in this case he wouldn't
find it. As he stares into the pit of despair, my voice
would come in at the end:

'Can't find that book on fly fishing? Then ring Dignitas

on 0041 blah blah blah, and We Will Take the Pain Away.'

I can imagine a series of adverts, all along the same lines:

'Fat? Then why not ring Dignitas...?'

'Just seen Ant and Dec's latest prime time show? Ring Dignitas...'

hello? Dignitas?

I wish they'd ring Dignitas!

'Falling in love with another man? Dignitas are only a phone call away...'

'Pizza delivery closed? Ring Dignitas now on...'

'One leg shorter than the other?' Well, you get my point.

WEDNESDAY 30TH JUNE

A bad day. Finally manage to get Gerry Adams and Ian Paisley together at the track to settle the Northern Irish Question. We were going to do it last month, but Paisley has had laryngitis after a day demanding rubber bin lids on the Bogside and an end to sodomy and Papal pig-sticking.

Unlike many in the world, I am not against Irishmen.
I can see they have their place - usually on the backs
of horses at Epsom or Cheltenham - but these two are a
surprise. Adams is a beardist and smells like the bottom
of a hamster's cage while Paisley is hugely fat and very
loud and drinks milk from the bottle.

I meet them at the track and tell them that I've been
to Belfast once. It was closed, I explain, except for a
Punch and Judy show being put on by a mournful Romanian
puppeteer who must have been on their equivalent of the
sex offender's register.

Neither can think of anything to say to that.

When they get on the track each is determined the
other won't get ahead and so they crash their cars into
one another before they get half way around. Each blames
the other and there is some pushing and shoving and it
is tempting to leave them to it. The Smeg even goes to
his garage to get bats into which he has driven a lot
of six-inch nails, so that they can hit each other all
the harder, but eventually Amil intervenes. After that
we hire each of them a taxi in Godalming and make them
sit in the back and then we set them off and wait to see
who wins. It turns out to be a draw even then, but the
thought of them droning on for another lap is too much
and we pay the cab drivers just to keep going all the
way to Holyhead.

So we haven't fixed Northern Ireland, which is a shame.

Amil is none too impressed with my 'Jeremy's Garage'
idea, either, but Zafira still thinks it's got legs, she
says, so long as we can get the Japs interested. They
love cruel telly and she thinks they'd hoot at the sight
of me telling a dwarf that he must now take off his

poly-cotton coverall and go home to his perverted foster parents because he mistook the gasket for the sump. She's looking to round up a collection of what we're going to call 'the eager disadvantaged' and after we've got them in the bag, all we'll need is a line like Alan Sugar's 'You're fired'.

She's still on at me about HomeGrown™ though. Now my hair is beginning to grow back, there does seem to be a sizeable chunk towards the top and the back missing. I shall customize the wig, with some nail scissors, and no one will ever know the difference. I'm good at that sort of thing.

FRIDAY 2ND JULY

I think I've worked out who Ron Trubshawe reminds me of: Charlie 'Groper' Godson, my prep-school French master. He has that same 1950s manner about him; the dark shag tobacco, the same sports jacket slick with human grease and the same telling aversion to soap.

I have to say, though, that his hygiene and dress sense weren't the only reasons (though they did come into it) that his 'extra French' lessons were so unpopular.

In fact, over the years I have tried to expunge

French Oral?

the memory of the Groper as you might try to shed the memory of, say, coming to in bed with a Genghis Khan of a hangover and a soreness south of the navel to discover that you're in bed with Janet Street-Porter, AND SHE'S JUST WAKING UP!

Let's just say that Groper's notion of 'French oral' differed in several critical respects from that of the Oxford and Cambridge examinations board. In fact his fumbling attempts to teach me something even less regular than a French irregular verb put me off France, the French and anything remotely gallic- or garlic-related - FOR LIFE.

You would!

And that was before I'd ever even heard of General de Gaulle, Zizi Jeanmaire, gîtes in the Aveyron, Raymond BlanketyBlank or Jean-Paul frigging Sarkozy.

Mind you. Carla Bruni, eh? Again. And then some. But only if she didn't play that guitar.

MONDAY 5TH JULY

The *BottomGear* Christmas Special is going to go

Not tonight, Carla

out live now! We're going to film it on 23rd December as we raid the Turkish prison! It will be INCREDIBLY exciting. Of course, we all feel bad for James mouldering so long in his dungeon, but it's going to take the monkeys at Land Rover that long to build their machine.

Why is it going to take them so long?

Because they are from the Midlands.

I mean, have you ever been there? Probably not. Most people just shut their eyes and mash their foot to the floor when they get past Oxford, hoping that nothing will get in their way until they are past the Keele Services.

Midlanders live in caves, you see, and can't write bum on the wall. It takes your average Midlander twice as long to say 'bowel movement' as it does to actually have one, a rare example of something being easier done that said.

√√√ √
One
of my
best!

But this is the norm up there. While they are still talking about how to build our machine, I could have circumnavigated the globe twice, in a Stannah Stairlift, with no batteries, backwards.

Come November the foreman will still be reading out our order to the boys on the factory floor and they'll be sitting in puddles of their own wee with their mouths hanging open, drooling onto their coveralls and wondering if they are holding a spanner or a sausage dog.

FRIDAY 9TH JULY

Rubbish day, the worst in television history. I fly to Geneva early to film a segment of the show in which I am supposed to see if it's possible to drive an Aston Martin DBS from Geneva to Milan for lunch and be back in time for tea. Of course it is, and who cares anyway, but it's Amil's idea and it gives us an excuse to tear through the Alps in a jowl-quiveringly fast car while making unsuitable comparisons to having sex with lap dancers and so on.

I know, I know, but there you are. It's a job, it needs to be done, and someone's got to do it.

Natasha and two cameramen are sitting back in economy while I'm in first with a beaker of gin and tonic in my hand and another Steven Seagal film on the 'in-flight infotainment system'. Even in first class the screen's so small I keep thinking I am watching Rammond, lifesize.

I am furious with him today.

He's got himself yet another show on prime time telly, something to do with children and Bunsen burners this time, even though I could swear he hasn't passed his nanny-state-sponsored child-fiddling certificate as required by law. He announced his new show at a production meeting and then afterwards told me that Baron Samedi was too busy to take on any new clients at the moment, but it might be worth asking him next year. All the time he was fingering that new necklace of his, so I am sure it is a voodoo thing.

Greater than Olivier?

Perhaps it's for the best, though? I mean, I am not sure how Zafira would take it if I fired her, but there must be something I can do. With my Levi's advertising scheme not working out, 'Jeremy's Garage' taking so long to get going, and now politics not exactly promising big bucks, it looks like I'll *have* to do that bloody HomeGrown™ campaign.

But bloody hell. Rammond. He really was just a nonentity until he had the crash, wasn't he? I mean, I am not just making that up am I? Before that, in terms of celebrity, I came in first. Then, lagging some way behind, James and Rammond came limping home, second equal, like losing contestants in the three-legged race at St Mungo's School for what we used to call the terminally spastic.

Never mind the turd in his pants, look at the size of his watch!

Then he has his crash and now people can't get enough of him. It's become him and me first, with James waddling home in third place, a long way behind, like the fat boy with a turd in his pants and sand in his shoes.

It makes me just a little bit angry.

So now here's what I've been thinking: if I could somehow organize a crash - maybe not as serious as Rammond's - in which I am temporarily knocked unconscious and have to be flown home to Chipping Norton, then I reckon I could regain my edge over him.

We land in Geneva with this thought still fizzing in my mind.

In the arrivals car park is the DBS, as polished and sleek as a titanium otter on steroids in a wind tunnel, and I whip out Zafira's list of 'Must Mention' words to try to come up with a description of my feelings on seeing it. The word ought to suggest something moist and sebaceous, *like* pre-ejaculatory fluid, but most definitely *not* pre-ejaculatory fluid.

I run down the list and find I am onto the word 'fuckmuffin'.

On the one hand I think this is going too far. And on the other I have no idea what it means. Does it even have a meaning? If I say 'this car looks and drives like a fuckmuffin', is that good? Or bad? I can't make up my mind.

I hastily tuck the list away.

After the technician rigs up the in-car camera I take the DBS south through the city and then along a boring stretch of motorway, letting them film me from the back of their hired Range Rover. Then we are up into the mountains and I am coming up with all my nonsense about this car being plenty exciting and then some, oh yes, and I am forcing it around hairpin bends at about 60 or 70 mph and it's all going well enough.

Pre-ejaculatory fluid?

It is then that I slide my Focus CD into the stereo and start to nod my head to the beat. The legendary track 'Hocus Pocus' will be the backing track to this segment because a quarter way through the tune, the lead flautist (how many bands have a lead flautist, hey?) takes his flute out and starts yodelling like a mentalist.

It is therefore perfect for the mountains.

Like Golden Earache, Focus are also Dutch.

I decide I've come around to the Dutch. Holland is the only country in Europe you can see from space after dark because they light every linear metre of their motorways, and the business about Anne Frank - well. Look. If I'd been the policeman who found her and if I'd've read her diary, well, maybe I'd've done exactly the same thing and dobbed her in.

Have you read it? It's awful. Truly awful.

No, really. If it was a car it'd be a Reva G-wiz.

I mean, think about it.

That's how to write history, Max Hastings!!

The Second World War was one of the most ball-braisingly ✓✓✓ exciting periods in history and here we have a commentary on it from a fifteen-year-old Dutch girl who only watched

COLLECTIBLE SPOONS
OF THE THIRD REICH

it hiding under the floorboards of a house in Amsterdam.

It is worse, even, than the other worst book about the war which I've got, which is Collectible Spoons of the Third Reich, by James A. Yannes.

Anyway, up through the mountains I go, and the views are pretty spectacular, but we're on the look-out for some Swiss cows to add the finishing visual clichés. I can see a sort of village up ahead, and a sign welcoming me to somewhere called Crans-Montana in fifteen different languages.

I am clipping along at about thirty miles an hour, I suppose, peering around looking for a barn or something where they might keep cows. It is then that out of the corner

The only witness

of my eye I see a flash of something khaki and orange. The next moment there is a slight crump from the offside front wheel and then one from the offside back wheel.

I slam on the ceramic anchors and get out.

There on the road behind the car is what I can only describe as a body.

The reason I can only describe it as a body is because it is just that, a body.

The Range Rover has come to a stop just beyond it and I can see Natasha staring with her hands clapped to her face. The cameraman is still leaning out of the window, his mouth open in shock.

I approach the body and bend down.

It looks like a little old man wearing a pale tan safari suit. He is lying on his front and he is not exactly moving. He appears, in fact, to be broken.

'Are you all right?' I ask, bending down.

There is no reply.

I gently turn him over and when I see his face I leap back.

It is Roger Moore.

I've just run over James Bond, and in an Aston Martin. Fuckmuffin.

SATURDAY 10TH JULY

Amil bails me out just after lunch and we fly home in silence.

The doctors still don't know if Roger Moore will live or die.

They won't let me see him.

It feels as if the whole world is on tenterhooks, just waiting, the clock ticking.

When I get home Zafira is out and the house is in darkness. HomeGrown™ have rung and cancelled their offer and there is a message on the phone from Ron Trubshawe about having a chinwag sometime soon.

It is the first time in my life when I know I have done something really, really bad, and do you know what? I don't like the feeling.

I console myself by a few hours of *Call of Duty* 4 and then I write a list.

If you had to run over a James Bond, which one would you run over first, and in which car would you choose to do it?

First would be Timothy Dalton, the worst Bond ever, and Welsh to boot, in a Vauxhall Vectra. Can anyone name another Timothy? No. You see? I rest my case. Being called Timothy is like being given a death sentence by your parents: you will be bullied all your life and little children will hate you. In comparison, being called Jeremy is like being called Sue. You have to be really tough to survive with a name like Jeremy.

√√√ *Title of my next bestseller?*

Unless you go into chartered surveying or land agenting, where you might thrive, but you might as well be dead anyway.

Second would be Pierce Brosnan. Stirling performances in *Mrs Doubtfire* and *Mamma Mia!*, but I'd still like to have him under the wheels of a Cherokee Jeep. The way he runs with his arms in the air, honestly, as if he had a honeycomb up his backside and he was being chased by homosexual honey bees.

Third would be Sebastian Bloody Faulks. Not because he played Bond, but just to stop him writing any more of his books so beloved of the so-called lesbian literati book groups.

Fourth is Daniel Craig in a Hummer H2 Geiger, sprayed orange with a wooden trim to match his acting. He's so chunky it'd need something with big wheels.

Fifth would have to be George Lazenby in a Holden Monaro. Least said about him the better, though that was a top film. You remember the Angels of Death? I've had 'em all, in my dreams.

Sixth Sean Connery. Scotch golfist. In a Jaguar XK.

Seventh Roger Moore. The very last Bond you'd want to squash, and yet...

SHAKEN NOT STIRRED!

Roger in a coma

TUESDAY 13TH JULY

Roger Moore still in a coma.

Write a column on how I regret running him over, but there are still reporters from every newspaper in the world at my gates in Oxfordshire and now they're even here in the Isle of Man. Long-range cameras in boats out to sea. U-boats sent by *Das Bild*. Helicopters overhead.

Depressed.

Zafira decides we should get away from it all and suggests a holiday.

But where?

You see, here's the thing about running over James Bond and then trying to get away from it all, which I admit is a pretty unusual situation in which to find oneself. Where would you want to go that he hasn't been to and wouldn't remind you of what you'd done?

Everywhere Zafira suggests reminds me of a Bond film.

Bahamas - all of them except for *From Russia with Love*.

Thailand - *The Man with the Golden Gun*.

Venice - *Casino Royale*.

The Moon - *Diamonds are Forever*.

Klosters - *On Her Majesty's Secret Service*.

On it goes. The only places they didn't bother with are Chad and the Milton Keynes snow bowl.

But how can I face taking a walk with Zafira across white sands under palm fronds, thinking all the while of

James Bond lying in a Swiss clinic with a sheet tucked
around his chest and a catheter up his todger?

Eventually we decide on a small island off the Italian
coast and Zafira books flights.

THURSDAY 15TH JULY

After a horrible flight we land in bright sunshine in
Naples, or Napoli as the locals call it, and just being
here makes me feel slightly more cheerful. We take a
taxi down to the port and while we wait for the boat
to take us out to our island we have a drink in one of
those cafés where a sip of beer costs the same as a
rummage in a Polish girl's pants, by which I mean about
£10.

Normally I like Italy. And it's not just the cars.
I like the set-up. I like the way the men wear ladies'
underpants and stack-heeled shoes. I like the way
these same men line up - the only time you'll ever
see an Italian take his turn, mind you - to dry-hump
Albanian refugees while
they're still on the beach
recovering from the swim
across the Adriatic. I like
the way they register their
disapproval of politicians by
hurling scaled-down versions
of cathedrals into their
faces.

I like, in short, almost
everything about them.

They have soul. They have
passion.

me: muff-diving in Corfu
last year

In fact if you liken Italy to U2, it's not 'The Unforgettable Fire'. It's not 'I Still Haven't Found What I'm Looking For'. It's 'Who's Gonna Ride Your Wild Horses', although I would have included the question mark at the end.

The island we're going to has a name but it is so secret that even if I knew it I couldn't tell you, in case you decided you'd like to come and stay here and spoil my view. There are, however, two almighty drawbacks: the first is that the island has no cars.

Zafira says this is a good thing. I should not, she says, be behind a wheel for a while.

The second is that it is largely given over to golfosexualists.

Golfosexualists are misogynists, of course, men who want to get away from their wives, but who are too fat or deranged to join the Territorial Army. Scratch any golfist on any pitch-and-putt in England and you'll find a repressed psychopath who never got over losing the

√√√
Too true!

empire, or a photocopier repair man trying to break into the big league, one of the two. Or possibly both.

When we get to the hotel - the only one on the island - the receptionist tells us we're very lucky to get a room. She is statuesque and I am looking at her chest through a narrow gap in her shirt, and so do not take in much of what she says. We go up to our room, which is the best

Buon Giorno!!!

in the hotel and costs more per night than a postman
earns in two years.

But now here's the thing.

What do you actually DO on a holiday like this?

I've bought a stack of books with pictures of guns
and explosions and well-upholstered blondes on the front,
but I've read them all already, or books just like them,
and as we sit by the pool and start to sizzle in the sun,
I become bored.

Boredom is bad for me.

I need something to do.

I see a couple of golfosexualists in Rupert Bear
trousers wielding mallets and trying to hit their small
balls into slightly bigger holes a long way off. I leap
to my feet and glare at them.

'Haven't they got anything better to do?' I ask Zafira,
who is reading one of her interminable novels
about the Tudors.

TYPICAL BUGGY

Golfosexualists

She looks up, looks at them, then says no, and returns to her book.

I've been here almost ten minutes and can hardly stand the silence.

Ping! The golfosexualists' balls go. Then they clamber into their buggy and - weeeeeee! - off it trundles towards another one of those pointless shaved holes at which they've aimed their ball. They're talking to one another and one of them laughs and I suddenly recall that scene in *Goldfinger* when Bond is being a golfist. That was Sean Connery of course, but I suppose Roger Moore used to play the game.

Until I ran him over that is.

I get a text from Amil. He says I'm to take my time. Then my editor at *The Times* rings. They've enough columns saved up and they can always run some old ones with a few words changed so there's no rush to get back.

I throw my phone down.

That's it. My career is over.

And all because of some geriatric in a tan suit and a bright orange face and marmalade-coloured hair.

I throw my book into the pool and pick up a paper.
Something in Italian. ¡¡Roger Moore, he still in coma!!
Pictures of tits everywhere, including, I see with a
swoop in my guts, one on page six. It is, of all the
people, Rammond - RAMMOND! - with his arm around some
dusky beauty, trying to look shy, trying to look as if
this is not all planned by Baron bloody Samedi. There is
some mention of him going to Hollywood too.

 That's it! Fuckmuffin to him!

 I need to drive a car.

 I march across the grass and while the golfosexualists
are gathered around their hole, complimenting one another
on their pastel tank tops, I duck into the buggy and mash
my foot down on the Axminster.

 The electric engine is feisty enough - it certainly
has more oomph than a G-wiz - and although she handles
with all the zip of a Wetherspoon public house and she's
got more understeer than a rodeo rider from *Brokeback
Mountain* (Zafira made me watch it!), I will say this for
her: as a getaway car she works perfectly. After about,
oh, three and a half weeks I am up to fifteen miles an
hour and the disappointed golf/man-lovers are a distant
speck in my non-existent rear view mirror.

 I sweep her up the grass and over a slight rise and
here I come to a stop.

 I look around me.

 Behind me the golfists have realized I've got their
buggy and are in hot pursuit. Zafira is on her feet by
the swimming pool, shading her eyes and looking worried.
In front of me is a long, perfectly manicured lawn
leading down to a line of palm trees and beyond is the
hotel's seawater swimming pool, which I didn't want to

use because salt water makes my hair frizzy. Beyond is the sea, shimmering blue, all the way to the horizon.

This is one of those moments when everything becomes clear. When you can see everything perfectly and you know there is only one thing to be done.

I give one last wave to Zafira, settle into the seat of the buggy, and floor it. With a fair wind and a bit of a slope I reckon I can top 20 mph. I am gripping the steering wheel and everything is a bit of a blur and to tell you the absolute truth I am hoping this won't hurt much.

It is not as fast as Rammond was going when he crashed, but he was wearing a crash helmet. And a seatbelt.

I aim for the middle of a group of three palm trees. They are regularly spaced and of identical size. I imagine I will get concussion, and will be in a coma for maybe a week or two. I imagine that I will get a scratch above my eye and will have to wear an eye patch for a month or two.

What I am not imagining - and this, to be honest, is where it all gets a little bit surreal - is that when the buggy hits the trees - which it does, oh yes, and then some - nothing happens.

That's right. Nothing happens.

You see, instead of exploding into a giant fireball, the buggy knocks the trees out of the way. They fly past, splintered and broken, as if

TYPICAL BUGGY, FLYING

they were mere stage props knocked up by a man called Nigel in a cashmere mix polo-neck.

For a moment I can't understand what has happened.

How have I managed to knock over three twenty-foot palm trees, with an electric-powered golf buggy?

It is while I am pondering this not exactly everyday question that I become aware that the whiney motor of the golf buggy has changed its tune.

You see the wheels are spinning, but there's nothing for them to hold onto. And that's because they are spinning in space.

I am, in short, flying.

For a moment it is the most wonderful feeling in the world, as if Kristin Scott Thomas invited you up to see her etchings and oh, can you bring a jar of honey, a marrow, and the girl who played Princess Leia in *Star Wars*?

But, just like Keith Moon, the party has to end sometime.

You see, you remember I mentioned there was a swimming pool? Well, that is more or less where I am now. I am in fact about fifteen feet above the pool, only now I'm falling like a sperm whale in a vacuum jar.

The splash is biblical. If God had managed anything

like that kind of splash in the Red Sea, he'd have got rid of the Egyptians *and* the Jews, so saving the world a hell of a lot of trouble.

But that is not what's bothering me at that moment.

No, you see, what's bothering me is that not only is the pool rather full of water, it is also rather full of people.

All of them are naked.

And all of them are men.

FRIDAY 16TH JULY

Gay porn.

I am, let me say this now, not against gay porn.

No, really. I am against wheelie suitcases, that's true. I am against fat women with frizzy hair, guilty. I am also against men who wear jewellery. I am against Premiership footballers who give their children silly names and I am even against Staffordshire, yes yes yes, all that is true. But I am not against gay porn.

No, really.

Having said that, I don't necessarily enjoy watching it. I'd rather watch it than, say, watch *Fifth Gear*, yes, but that's like saying I'd rather watch gay porn than spend two weeks locked in a Prestwick council house with Susan Boyle.

Yet here I am, sitting next to Zafira in the hotel's private cinema, with about twenty or thirty very well-built, very closely shaved, young men. The smell of aftershave and pheromones and something else is thick in the air, and we are all of us settling down to watch some gay porn.

It's a film with the working title *In at the Gay End*. It is only being made thanks to a grant from the thousand-year EuroReich, which has seen fit to divert our tax pounds into gay pornography, and for what?

> BEST PORN FILM TITLES: THE SHORTLIST
>
> 1. Driving Into Miss Daisy
> 2. Shaving Ryan's Privates
> 3. Schindler's Fist
> 4. Breast Side Story
> 5. Gangbangs of New York

To undermine the Americans, of course.

Peter Mandelson's idea: naturally.

Which means it is rubbish.

All these men around me are the cast and crew of the film, and until yesterday they were happily shooting it down by the seawater pool. Now the director - a chubby little Frenchman called Raoul - is on stage explaining that we are going to see the rushes of that day's shooting.

We are at the scene, he says, when the hero of the piece, an international water-polo player called something like Blade Tuxedo - played here by the internationally renowned gay porn star Clint Thrust, who stands up and acknowledges the applause like the star he is - with his career in freefall after a terrible mix-up with a butt-plug at the Olympic Games, finds himself

BEST PORN STAR
NAMES: THE SHORTLIST

1. Clint Thrust

2. Flick Shagwell

3. Ben Dover

4. Long Dong Silver

5. Tony Eveready

6. Jeremy Klaxon

washed up on a mysterious men-only island where no one recognizes him. Blade is minding his own business oiling his very impressive pecs in the pool when the villain, Dag, thinks he is eyeing up Dag's boyfriend, Lars.

For no very obvious reason Dag then challenges Blade to a water-polo match. What ensues will surprise no one who has seen *The Mighty Ducks*, *1*, *2* and *3*, and after Blade slots home the winning goal, the teams start kissing and very soon we are deep in orgy land.

As I say, a rubbish film. Even *Shaving Ryan's Privates* was better than this.

'So,' Raoul is saying, 'these are rough cuts of the scene, but you will still notice some verrry hot man-on-man action, and I think we can all congratulate ourselves on that front, but thanks to Jeremy here, the scene is transformed into something very *extra special*.'

The boys all clap and cheer and one or two of them pat me on the shoulder and then Raoul nods to Anton behind the projector and as the lights go out, the film starts up.

At this point I cover my eyes.

Even the noise is horrific, though, like the sound of a
Turk wrestling half a hundredweight of butter while in
the background his halfwit sister is bound and gagged,
with a spider crawling up her leg.

The men around me are moving restlessly and the air
feels much warmer than it ought. I still can't watch.
I grip Zafira's arm but she shakes my hand off. She is
still too ashamed of me.

Then, over all the gulching and slurping, comes the
noise of three balsa wood trees being broken into pieces
and scattered everywhere. There is the scream of an
electric motor and four 12" wheels dry-running in mid-
air.

It is, of course, my golf cart.

In the film you can see my face. I am screaming, half
in naked terror, half in ecstatic delight. My face looks
like Bonnie Langford's, pickled in a medicine jar.   ✓✓✓ Yes!

Then the buggy crashes down and how it doesn't kill
any of them I'll never know.

I suppose they were just lucky.

Sometimes God actually does smile on homos.

Water erupts around the cart, washing some of the
homosexualists out of the pool onto the side and then
rushes back in to cover the cart as it sinks too quickly
for me to get out.

The cameras keep rolling.

There is total silence except for gentle whining from
one of them who has what looks to be a nasty graze on
the side of his willy.

'OMG,' someone mutters off-camera, 'what was that?'

Then Zafira arrives over the crest of the hill.

Suddenly there is a lot of shouting and screaming and

Thrust to the rescue

wailing, but amid all the chaos there is something missing.

Exactly. There is still no me. I am quite obviously still under the water.

Then the camera cuts to Clint Thrust, who understands I must be saved.

The camera follows him as he dives in. He is gone for a moment. There are a lot of bubbles, and then two heads emerge.

I am unconscious, but Clint has saved me.

My hair has gone frizzy, and I look like a lesbian in a lightning storm.

Clint drags me to the side of the pool where his friends lay my lifeless body on my back. For a moment next to those tanned and taut bodies, I see my own and I give thanks that the Japanese whaling fleet is not in sight.

The camera follows Zafira now, as she bends over me and starts pounding my chest with her fists. No wonder it was a bit sore this morning. And I thought I must have hit the golf buggy's steering wheel.

'You fucking idiot!' she is screaming. 'You fucking childish twat!'

It is all extremely unsettling, seeing your own apparent death caught on film, with your wife-cum-manager trying to help the process along, but it is nothing to what comes next.

Clint, still naked, is on his knees next to me. The tip of his penis is no more than a foot from my ear-hole. The camera makes it look vast, like one of James Might's hand-tooled brogues: the same colour

Sausage

and just as knobbly, though without the punched holes.

Then Clint shuffles forward, bends over and starts to give me mouth-to-mouth resuscitation.

It reminds me, briefly, of that night in Germany...

I can still hardly bring myself to watch.

Then it gets worse. The boy who plays right defence in the game of water polo, also naked, moves Zafira aside.

'Ve must start de CPR,' he says in an Austrian accent that Zafira knows she must obey. Now, the last Austrian I let touch my semi-naked body was a man dressed as a woman in a club in Hamburg specializing in what the Americans call Cleethorpes steamers, and for a moment this seems no different.

The boy straddles my hips, his sizeable, though now thankfully slightly flaccid, member resting on my tummy like a pork loin on a butcher's block, and he starts cardiopulmonary resuscitation, grunting vigorously as he does so.

SUNDAY 18TH JULY

No one will answer my calls at the BBC. It can mean only one thing: the holidays. In July whole streets,

whole boroughs - or villages as they like to think of
them - in North London simply empty out. They become
ghost villages. The residents pack their expensively
and pointlessly reconditioned Volkswagen camper vans
with clothes they've bought from Mini Boden and food
they've bought from Waitrose and they begin their annual
migration west, to Cornwall.

In the first few days of the month the M4 looks like
the Serengeti Plain when the wildebeest head north
or south or wherever it is they go. The Hammersmith
roundabout acts as that river in which the crocodiles
lurk, waiting to devour the halt and the lame.
Whenever I see it I keep expecting to hear lush music
in the background and David Attenborough's whispery
tones explaining what's going on. It is here that the
radiators will overheat and the windows will fall out,
he'll say. It is here that Tarquin and Ottoline will
start biting one another, and it is here that the wife
will stab her husband in the throat with a biro because
he forgot to pack the gin. And why? Because they think
that without this annual migration their lives would,
simply, not-be-worth-living.

Meanwhile all of us who are too poor or too sensible
to go on holiday in August stay at home, basking in the
silence of unexpectedly quiet streets, or we go to pubs
where we can sit in an actual chair at an actual table
and have a pint of beer without being given the benefit
of some blue-sky thinking from a chap in the BBC IT
department wearing square-framed glasses, fun shorts and
a colourful top.

But if it isn't Cornwall then it's Norfolk, and that,
for my money, is even worse.

So much has been said about people from Norfolk that it seems unfair to add to their inbred woes, but since only a handful can read or write and the others are too busy planning their own suicides, I ought to admit that I once kissed a girl from King's Lynn. Afterwards she told me that wasn't how her brother did it and I've never been back since.

A mediarast in a colourful top

On my way to the car from the airport arrivals I manage to step in dog shit. Gives me an idea for my next column.

MONDAY 19TH JULY
Roger Moore is out of his coma.

From his hospital bed he issues a statement to tell the world that he's forgiven me and, having seen the footage of my time with Clint and the water-polo team - which is all over the interwebster of course - he understands that I have my

Norfolk

own demons with which to wrestle. He goes on to make a
special plea to the world's assembled media that I never
be allowed back into Switzerland.

I agree, but only on condition he comes out of
retirement to race against the other Bonds.

I am a genius.

Ron Trubshawe is back in touch.

'Not being allowed back into that dump'll only boost
your chances, Jazza, old horse,' he says in that weirdly
familiar voice of his. 'People hate the Swiss. All that
Nazi gold. And your adventure on Dr Moreau's island of
gay pornography's landed you the pink vote on a plate.
I'd like to see how the blasted Liberal Democratic
Communists come back at you for that!'

I wonder if now is the right time to tell him about
what happened in Germany. I am about to open my mouth
to say something when his money runs out again and he's
cut off.

Zafira has spread it around that my accident was a bid
for suicide brought on by guilt at having nearly killed
James Bond. She's organized some sympathetic profiles in
a couple of the Sunday papers and I've said I am sorry,
and that I wished it had been Timothy Dalton, and with
that the world seems ready to forgive me.

FRIDAY 23RD JULY

The election is only a few days away and I've never been
so busy. All day Ron and I drive through Chipping Norton
with a speaker strapped to an Alfa Romeo Brera Coupe V6,
shouting through a microphone. That way I'm killing two
birds with one stone, since not only can I broadcast my
message, I can knock out a quick review as well.

'Vote Klaxon!' I shout. 'Vote Klaxon on 29th July! Vote Klaxon to clear your streets of parakeets. No more parakeets, ladies and gentlemen! No more wheelie-bins either. Vote Klaxon to rebuild Hadrian's Wall, ladies and gentlemen, vote Klaxon to move Birmingham to Alabama. Bit of understeer there. Only Klaxon will make the Belgians take Wales back. Only Klaxon guarantees a penny-in-the-pound tax rise for chemistry teachers, and tuppence for men who wear square-toed shoes. Only Klaxon will guarantee the freedom of cannibals to advertise on the internet. Only Klaxon promises a ban on Cherie Lunghi, veganist weddings, origami and peat-free compost. Flappy-paddle gearbox! Only Klaxon can do this, ladies and gentlemen. Only Klaxon will make Kirstie Allsopp mayor of Bratislava. Only Klaxon will forbid the sale of sauerkraut on garage forecourts. Only Klaxon will make ornithology a sackable offence, ladies and gentlemen, and only Klaxon will hold a referendum on whether or not we should rename Kai Rooney.'

VOTE KLAXON

IF YOU DON'T VOTE KLAXON ON 29TH JULY, THEN YOU'RE A TWAT

Some of this comes from the top of my head, obviously, depending on what I see as we chug along.

'Klaxon will ban tracksuits and thongs on fat girls, ladies and gentlemen. No more muffin tops on show with Klaxon! No more wigs, either, like that one there. Wheelchairs will be a thing of the past with Klaxon!'

Funny thing is that even though I haven't the slightest thing in common with 'The Man on the Clapham Omnibus', everyone I talk to says that although they don't agree with everything I say they'll still vote for me.

No, really. I am sorry, but am I missing something here?

'They'll vote for anyone who promises to benefit the people they think they'll be next year,' is how Ron explains it. 'Offer a tax break to people earning over £100K and everybody'll vote for it because they all think that next year they'll be earning £100K.'

Have to stack a lot of shelves for that sort of wonga.

I am particularly proud of my election poster, which has a picture of me in a white t-shirt and a leather jacket looking like a puzzled gonad and underneath runs the strapline: 'If you don't vote Klaxon on 29th July, then you're a cunt!'

SUNDAY 25TH JULY

Only a few days to go.

I can scarcely speak. It's as if I've been eating nothing but wire-wool, Ex-Lax and krill for the last two weeks. I haven't had a solid poo for a month and even my tears have turned brown.

Nor have I been to the studio for a week. I missed Jonathan Sacks making up for Benjamin Netanyahoo's rubbish performance in his reasonably priced car last month by walloping the crap out of a man called Rasoul Movahedian who's apparently the Iranian ambassador to the Court of St James. Nearly lapped him, Amil said.

So it is one-all between the Jews and the Arabs then.

Not sure that it produced any conclusion though. Being Jewish is better than being Muslim? Seems a touch vague to me, but of course that's what a lot of this so-called Middle Eastern nonsense boils down to in the end, isn't it?

I mean, think about it. It isn't Yahweh against Allah - although if we could get them in the cars that would really be something - it's just some tribe whacking another tribe and looking

UNSUITABLE GARMENTS FOR FAT GIRLS: THE SHORTLIST

Thongs

Suspenders

Thigh-length boots

Hot Pants

Crop tops

Boob tubes

GREECE IS A TOILET

for a reason to do it the wife'll swallow.

Talking of Rasoul Movahedian, I don't think he can be a Muslim. To be a Muslim you have to have the same name as at least a million other Muslims. You have to be called Mohammed Something or other, or Imran Khan. Back in the Middle Ages everyone in Britain was called Thomas or John, of course - even if they were a woman - but now we are all called Kai or Germaine or Jaydon or Benzine. Benzine is something you don't hear too much of these days, either. It used to be all over the shop and now you'd be hard pressed to know what it is. It's like the threat of nuclear war, a relic of a time and a place.

Which brings me nicely onto John Littledick, my fellow party member, prospective poor man's Klaxon for Barking and Dagenham. He'll never beat the BNP because of Nick Griffin and that workshy, jobdodging eye of his. You see, thanks to rules laid down by our Belgian masters in Brussels, anyone with a dicky eye is legally entitled to a few years in power.

✓✓✓✓
Too
true!!

It's the only way to explain Gordon Brown.

THURSDAY 29TH JULY

Election Day.

The polling station is in a local school. I've got this one marked for closure because the so called 'head teacher' - a lesbian *and* a woman - got the kids to knit bike racks to celebrate the Winterval solstice and then dedicated them to Gaia in a non-denominational Druid ceremony to which I was not invited. I'll sell the building to a chap called Giles so he can turn it into a

Vegetablists praying to the Giant Mushroom in the Sky

Bangladeshi cinema and soup club on Wednesday nights and with the money I get from that I'll buy up the organic porcupine sanctuary or whatever it is near the village green and grant a licence for Shell or BP to plant GM tobacco or dig for oil.

Anyway, I've managed to get Amil to shoot a mini *BottomGear* challenge today. He was a bit doubtful at first, but I get to the track early and there is Rammond dressed like a teenaged dwarf-wrangler and we stand around insulting each other's mothers for a bit until two minibuses pull up. One is a yellow American school bus-type thing, the other is a Hino Poncho.

I act surprised.

'What's this?' I say as the runner gives me the envelope. 'A mini-challenge?'

Rammond has to look as if he can't believe it.

'What are they like?' he says, shaking his head.

I choose the school bus while Rammond takes the Hino Poncho. This is apt. They look the same, Rammond and this bus. I pretend yet more surprise as once again we are told to decorate our vehicles with funny slogans like, 'I prefer buggery', and 'Yoohoo I'm gay'. I call my minibus 'Fanny', Rammond calls his 'Cnut' and we all laugh until we wet our pants. Natasha looks away. She is wearing a mackintosh and a pair of Wellington boots.

We can hear noise coming from The Smeg's garage but no one is brave enough to go in. There is the

The Smeg cooking pigs' cheeks

smell of sulphur and boiling meat. He must be having one of his parties again. He does that now and again, cooking huge vats of pigs' cheeks and chitterling sausage, getting in cases and cases of re-conditioned Hoffmeister beer. Never invites me.

While the crew get to work on decorating the buses Rammond and I stand around telling one another how we each saw the other's mum in *Readers' Wives* until the runner turns up again with more Challenge details in an envelope.

Once more I open it and read my own handwriting.

'You'll never believe this, Rammond,' I say, 'but we've got to take our minibuses and collect as many people registered to vote and drive them to a polling station in Chipping Norton!'

'No way!' he is scripted to say. 'That is the maddest cap thing I have ever heard!'

He is wearing so much product on his hair it has set up a strange electric storm, with sparks jumping from frond to tress, and he walks around in his own micro-climate.

So after that we climb into the minibuses, quickly scrape them against one another, 'as you do', and then set off for Chipping Norton. On the way I insult minibus drivers, suggesting they're fully signed-up members of the Under-Eights Club, which, like all Belgians, they mostly are. Then we find a hedgehog to run over and a historic churchyard gate to knock down and an old almshouse to inadvertently set on fire and it is all shaping up very nicely.

An ex-hedgehog

Rammond drives through town trying to round up voters like the Child Catcher in *Chitty Chitty Bang Bang*, but I use my local knowledge and head straight for the plague pits. Ron is up there with about fifteen pensioners and the smell of wee is strong. By now the minibus windows are all starred and shattered and the back door has fallen off after a hilarious run-in with an old oak tree, so they are a bit reluctant to get in.

BOMB
CLEETHORPES

I tell them there is some bacon inside and in they climb.

They talk to me as we drive.

'I don't agree with everything you say,' each one takes his turn to say, 'but you always speak your mind, so I'll vote for you.'

Once again I wonder if I am missing something here.

One of them tells me about his Austin Princess.

'Have you ever driven a four-wheel drive car?' I ask him.

He shakes his head as if I'd just asked him if he'd ever copped a BJ from Zara Phillips.

'Ooooh, no,' he says, 'I've never driven another car than my Princess, but I wouldn't miss an episode of *BottomGear*.'

None of it makes any sense of course, but that hardly matters, because at the polling station I hear the same pro-Klaxon refrain: 'I disagree with what you say, but I will vote for you because I admire what you say in your columns.'

I can say anything! Greece is a toilet! The French are all homosexuals! Footballers shouldn't wear gloves in bed! Shakespeare? - I'd rather haemorrhage! Righty tighty, lefty loosey. People who can't afford to send their children to Eton are pointless. Let's bomb Uruguay back to the Stone Age. No! - make it Paraguay. Better still, Cleethorpes - it's nearer! Mars bars are better than Milky Ways by a factor of ten to three! Why I'll never fist a vegetablist! Shackling people from Devon makes sense. I'd rather sleep with a pig than learn German. Why we shouldn't have dinosaur museums in Dorking.

None of it makes sense, as I say, and yet here they are, shaking my hand.

Only one person suggests I should have used paraffin to blow up that badger. He also suggests that I shouldn't have put my finger up my bottom and 'rootled around'.

I wish I hadn't too. Or at least I wish I'd never told anyone about it.

Still, he shakes my hand, even though I've still not washed it.

After they've voted we canvass them as they come out. If they tell us they voted for Klaxon and the EFDC then they get 90p to spend on a cup of tea or the bus back to their squalid little hovels, whichever they choose.

I get Rammond on the radio.

FREE NACHOS FOR THE ELDERLY

'Where are you?'

Of course he has no idea. He's probably in the hair-care aisle of the Hemel Hempstead branch of Boots as usual.

I'D RATHER SLEEP WITH A PIG THAN LEARN GERMAN

By the time polling closes I have driven twenty-three busloads of the criminally infirm, impoverished and terminally bone idle to the polling station and I am pretty confident that not only have I won the *BottomGear* mini-challenge, but just possibly the election.

FRIDAY 30TH JULY

Another very odd day.

It all starts early. Or to be precise, it starts at midnight, when the Returning Officer summons us to announce the result of yesterday's election. After spending the better part of the evening in the pub with Ron using my iPhone to send pictures of our knobs to John Littledick we're a bit dizzy, shall I say, and as we go in I notice some of the people I drove to the polling station are still slumped at the bus stop. They're waiting for the last bus that will never turn up.

They look a bit of a mess, to be honest, and if I get in I'll have the light in the bus stop removed so this sort of thing doesn't happen again.

In the hall there are hundreds of television cameras and every newspaper in the land has sent someone to cover the result. Rammond is there, goofing about for the reporters like a meerkat with bipolar disorder.

'Rammond!' I snap, 'What are you doing here?'

'Just came to lend my support,' he says, 'as you do.'

He's fingering that voodoo necklace and grinning as if this is the best fun in the world.

'For fuck's sake, Rammond. I'm trying to run a serious campaign here and you're just cocking about like a Scotchman at a creditor's funeral!'

'Don't be like that, Jeremy. To tell you the truth I have to be here. My agent, you know?'

'You're just trying to get all the attention as usual! I'm going to get the Sergeant-at-Arms or whatever to throw you out.'

'I wouldn't do that, Jeremy, not if I were you. You see, I might just have a word with that journalist over there. Tell him about my memoirs. Tell him about - '

And here he rolls those bloody eyes of his, as if I don't know what's coming next.

'- Tell him about what happened in Germany.'

I breathe deeply.

'All right. You can stay. But only for five minutes.'

A reporter interrupts to ask me about some policy or other - free nachos for the elderly? Make Scotland dark all the time? - but then gets onto the latest *BottomGear* challenge that ended with me hilariously parking my bus in the middle of the River Evenlode and calling the fire brigade to come and rescue me in one of their heat-seeking helicopters.

The Returning Officer has a comb-over, eyebrows that look as if they belong

√√√ Fuck off, Alex Salmond!!

BIPOLAR MEERKAT

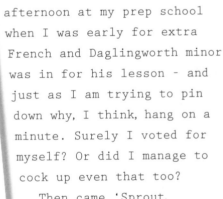

elsewhere on his body, and beefy murderer's hands. He welcomes everybody to the hall in his comical country accent, but he is looking extremely uncomfortable and when he starts reading out the names, it is clear why. David Abercrombie-Smythe (Conservative): 3 votes. Steve Bloke (Labour): 2. On it goes, name after name, none of them getting into double digits.

Then it is just me and some hippy in cord loon pants and speccy glasses representing the anybody-but-Klaxon crowd of assorted fruit worshippers and po-faced bum-bandits.

'Klaxon, Jeremy (Freedom for English Democratic Values Party, or something): 0 votes.'

There is a gasp. I hear Ron choking - a sort of strange gargle that for some reason takes me back to an afternoon at my prep school when I was early for extra French and Daglingworth minor was in for his lesson - and just as I am trying to pin down why, I think, hang on a minute. Surely I voted for myself? Or did I manage to cock up even that too?

Fruit worshipper

Then came 'Sprout, Reinhardt (Associated ultra-fruitarians); 43,465 votes.'

There is fruit-inspired pandemonium in one corner of the hall as Sprout collapses from exhaustion brought on by not having ever had an animal in his sights while holding a knife and fork.

But surely that's not right?

It must be a fix, and yet just a glance at Reinhardt Sprout tells you he could not fix a drink, let alone a ballot box. We are all standing looking around trying to work out what's happened.

'I say,' says Abercrombie-Smythe (Conservative) 'can that be right, do you think? I mean I put in four votes myself.'

The Returning Officer is as confused as a nun at a circumcision party and the beige-teated vote-counters with their boxes of ballots are scratching their blue-rinsed heads. Meanwhile there's a full-scale riot as the reporters all rush to get out on the grass and send in reports that suggest that far from being the popular millionaire with the unashamedly self-interested touch that endears him to one and all, Jeremy Klaxon is the most hated man in Oxfordshire, if not in the whole wide world.

Zafira picks me up in the Range Rover and drives me home.

A consolation text from John Littledick on my phone. He didn't get a single vote either, and so it seems that after Fred West we are the second equal least popular men in Britain.

I am sick in the footwell.

SATURDAY 31ST JULY

It was Rammond! RAMMOND!

Rammond switched the ballot boxes around! Not himself, of course, but some of the even-smaller-than-him little production gnomes did it to publicize his new kids' programme *As You Do*.

On the one hand I could easily kill him because the originals were thrown out and so there'll have to be another election - and so I'll have to do more campaigning - but on the other hand, as Zafira points out, at least people don't, after all, hate me quite as much as they do John Littledick.

Rammond, though, is in deep trouble. His stunt has brought him a lot of attention and I dare say the ratings will be good, but he's facing a terrifyingly large fine for election fraud and, since he's used BBC money to do it, he could be given his marching orders.

Of course I wish him well, but if he were to get the bullet - and it's a pretty serious offence, election fraud, I imagine - then I'd be free to choose anyone I liked to replace him. I mean I'd need to replace him. Who could I get? It wouldn't have to be someone who knew anything about cars - I'm pretty sure the only person that knows anything about them is in fact Natasha - and *it needn't be a man*!

What about that girl in the pub?

Svetlana.

I've made one star - two if you count James, which I don't - so why not another?

Her eyes are close-set, that is true, but I dreamt about her the other day. It was a strange dream. I was part of a crowd waiting around a dry swimming pool and in the bottom of the pool was a silver bucket. After a fanfare, Svetlana came onto the diving board, wearing a purple gown edged with white fur. We all clapped and cheered and she waved at us and was smiling. Then she turned around and walked backwards to the edge of the diving-board and then squatted and aimed a huge turd - and it was startlingly lengthy for

Svetlana -
the future of BottomGear?

a lady - right into the bucket, fully ten metres below.

I woke up cheering my head off.

It could be a sign, couldn't it?

I mean I got James and Rammond their jobs on less.

MONDAY 2ND AUGUST

Disaster.

It looks like from now on I'll be running my election on my own.

You see, now Ron - or Charlie as I should have called him all along - has been arrested.

He was holding a press conference with John Littledick demanding a similar recount in Barking because he couldn't believe Littledick wouldn't get a single vote (although as I tried to tell him, not even Littledick is a big enough cunt to vote for John Littledick when someone - Daglingworth minor, probably - recognized Ron

as the French master who'd once taught him the irregular
verb to drop one's trousers and take it like a good'un.

I knew I'd seen him before.

Anyway, this snitch rang the police and half an hour
later they arrived to cart poor old Ron off, just as
he was giving another interview about his work for the
Scouts.

If you were being murdered or deflowered by an armed
gang it'd take the police half way until next week to
come around of course, and always while you're out, but
give them the chance to arrest someone famous in front
of the cameras then they're there in a shot.

Not that Ron was famous, of course.

You see, it was the name Trubshawe that flummoxed me.
I've only met one Trubshawe before. The Concorde test
pilot, who - alongside Isambard Kingdom Brunel, the bloke
who designed the Spitfire, the late lamented Paul Raymond,
the incomparable Nigel Mansell and the original line-up
of Genesis - if you took the e from the end of his name,
was one of the ten greatest Britons in history.

So no wonder I didn't properly recognize the old
pederast.

I'd've thanked him if I had.

Best years of my life.

TUESDAY 3RD AUGUST

The election is rerun and this time, thanks to all the
television cameras and all the fuss from the North
London media types, the old folks all turn up at the
polling station without me having to bus them there.
Some of them have been stuck there since last Thursday
anyway, still waiting for the bus that will never come.

GREAT BRITISH MEN: THE SHORTLIST

1. Isambard Kingdom Brunel
2. R.J. Mitchell (if you don't know he's the bloke who designed the Spitfire, then you're gay)
3. Brian Trubshaw (Concorde test pilot)
4. Peter Gabriel
5. Tony Banks
6. Phil Collins
7. Steve Hackett
8. Mike Rutherford
9. Nigel Mansell
10. Margaret Thatcher

(1970 Genesis line-up)

The results are read out by the same apprentice murderer as last time and this time it seems the popular will finds its true expression, by a majority of 23,749.

'I therefore declare that Jeremy Klaxon is duly elected as Member of Parliament for Mid-Oxfordshire North-West!'

A triumph! An epic, testicle-tickling, tongue-on-your-perineum triumph!

There is a tremendous roar, louder than a backfiring Cosworth with split ends and I go and find Reinhardt Sprout and place my leather-soled driving slipper on his grubby socked toe.

MY TESTICLE-TICKLING ELECTION TRIUMPH:
THE FIGURES

Abercrombie-Smythe, David (Conservative): 5148 votes

Bloke, Steve (Labour): 212 votes

Bluebell, Caroline (Green Party): 456 votes

Naive, Nicholas (Liberal Democratic Party) 1076 votes

Klaxon, Jeremy (Freedom for English Democratic values
    Party): 28,897 votes

Sprout, Reinhardt (Associated Ultra-Fruitarians): 105 votes

'That's for you, veggie-boy,' I say.

Then I drive back home in a Ferrari F430, *Hooked on Classics* blasting from the stereo, the Sat Nav set to Downing Street.

It is true that I then prang the front off-side of the Ferrari's bodywork on the van belonging to the men flattening the speed bump at the bottom of my drive, but that's what I call power.

Zafira is lying in bed ready to be made love to by a Right Honourable MP, but just as I am bounding up the stairs with a semi, the new Prime Minister with his wafer-thin majority rings to congratulate me on the result. As an independent I know he needs me on his side, so I wait to hear what he is going to offer me.

√√√ Ok, Dave?

The position I really want is chief pleasurer
to his wife as she is bent over a hay bale
wearing nothing but a pair of expensive
leather riding boots and a dab of Deep Heat
behind each ear.

He goes on for a bit, talking about his Vulva
D40 and the traffic on the M4, and I worry for a
moment that he might offer me Transport, about
which I know even less than I do about Sanskrit.
Then he starts talking about some old column I
bashed out about stepping in dog shit.

'Dog lovers are very important to us,
Jeremy,' he says, 'but equally we hear what
you've been saying, so Oliver and I have come up with the
ideal post for you.'

He then offers me the job of Minister for Dogs.

Jeremy Klaxon, MP and Dog Shit Tsar.

THURSDAY 5TH AUGUST

Yessssssssssss! The BBC have finally seen sense and bowed
to public demand.

Rammond has been sacked!

Amil rang last night to say that after seeing the
Director General Rammond came to the production office
to pick up his spare bottle of Joop! and about a half a
hundredweight of hair product, but that he didn't sound
too upset. He must have something up his sleeve.

Of course I've been on the radio all morning saying
I think it's stupid, an example of the nanny state gone
mad, and I've invited the DG outside for a fight. Zafira
says you can't hear the laughter in my voice, but all I
can think of is who to replace him with.

What might have been: Jeremy and the Coalitionists

1. Unknown

2. Ian Duncan Smith: IDS? IBS more like.

3. Theresa May: looks like her brother James and you most definitely wouldn't, though I suppose someone must have.

4. Liam Fox: Scotch dwarf. A poor man's David Steel, and then some.

5. Unknown

6. David Willetts: rumoured to have two brains.

7. Vince Cable: ballroom-dancer, possibly socialist, looks like big-ears off of the telly, and with a similar grasp of supply and demand.

8. George Osborne: a milk-skinned mummy's boy, probably spent most of his life with a kick me sign stuck to his back.

9. Unknown. Looks like he dines on the blood of virgins, and enjoys it.

10. Lord Strathclyde: Scotch fattist previously good only for ship's ballast.

11. William Hague: slaphead from Planet Mekon with a face like a pre-sucked Werther's Original. Why is he back? Didn't he get the message last time?

12. Unknown fattist. Head like a shipping buoy, probably just as dangerous.

13. Andrew Lansley: Looks like Swiss Tony.

14. David Cameron: The Fat Controller with the flappy-paddle handshake that comes from being a cyclist (but hot wife whom I'd like to watch during the harvest, if you know what I mean, when it's hot and she is sweating down her back and her shirt is clinging to her and ⌐⌐⌐

15. Unknown
16. Michael 'Call me Mike' Gove: looks like a vet about to fist a cow, or a cow about to fist a vet, two things that look surprisingly similar.
17. Nicholas Clegg: The Fat Controller's glove puppet (hot wife, though possibly Spanish), proud to be A Very Useful Engine.
18. Unknown
19. Unknown sari-ist. Probably one of those 'clever wimmin', so you probably wouldn't.
20. Unknown
21. Unknown, but he's got wet eyes, like a fawn, so you want to blast him with a 12 bore.
22. Unknown 23. Unknown 24. Unknown 25. Unknown
26. Danny Alexander: Scotch ginger, should still be doing sums at school.
27. Ken Clarke: fattist Europhilic 'toe-tapping' jazzist; catchphrase 'what happens east of Calais, stays east of Calais'. Not to be trusted even with a shopping trolley.
28. Unknown
29. ME! Dog Shit Tsar (and another hot wife!).
30. Unknown. Is he wearing a corset? Or is he just very pleased to see me?
31. Unknown

FOREIGN/LEFT-WING/PONCEY DOGS I WILL BAN AS DOG SHIT TSAR

- Miniature poodle
- Shih-tzu
- Chihuahua
- Dachshund
- Laika
- Schnauzer

Svetlana? She's on my shortlist, which I have been working - I said WORKING - on, as are, in no particular order:

1. Yasmine Bleeth. She played Caroline Holden in *Baywatch*, do you remember? Fantastic show. Why don't they make them like that anymore? I've still got the theme tune on my iPod: 'I'm Always Here', sung by Jimi Jamison of Survivor, though most stupid people think David Hasselhoff sang it, which replaced the original theme tune - which I've also got - 'Save Me' sung by Peter Cetera, with Bonnie Raitt on guitar and Richard Sterban, the bass singer for The Oak Ridge Boys, as the background vocalists. I was going to choose Pamela Anderson instead of La Bleeth, of course,

but discovered her insurance doesn't cover her travelling in the front seats of cars with air bags.

2. Sandra Bullock. Another American, I know, but she's neither fat nor unwelcome in my

bed, if you know what I mean, and she can drive a bus. No really. Did you see her in *Speed*? What a film. 120 minutes in a bus and no one smelling of wee. *Speed 2*, not so good.

3. Liz Hurley. Acted off the screen by inanimate objects I know, but remember those pneumatics in that dress she wore? That cunt in *Four Weddings and a Funeral* is still smiling about it. I wouldn't mind jacking her up and checking out her Front End, is my point.

4. Queen Rania of Jordan. Possibly a Towelheadist, but you would, wouldn't you?

Derby winner

5. Keira Knightley. Body like a derby winner, and I don't mean Lester Piggott.

6. Elle MacPherson. So wickedly sexy that she can only have come from criminal stock.

MONDAY 9TH AUGUST

The American I most admire is Thomas Sullivan Magnum IV, P.I.

No, really.

You'll say that *Magnum P.I.*'s made up and that someone like Martin Luther Kong or Chevy Chase or Dwight P. Roosevelt is more worthy, but I've got every series of *Magnum, P.I.* on VHS and I try to watch an episode every Sunday after lunch. I'll tell you this about him: his real stroke of genius wasn't the extravagant moustaches or the epic dress sense, nor the free access to Robin Masters's fleet of cars that included a Ferrari 308 GTS

as well as an Audi 5000 C3 and a Jeep Wagoner. No, his
real stroke of genius was to work when he felt like it,
and not when he didn't.

With James in prison and Rammond in the wilderness
with no replacement in sight, Amil is making me do
all the boring stuff, like go to factories and drive
ordinary cars in pointless challenges that we used to
make Rammond do. Can a Honda Accent hold more ping pong
balls than a gorilla? Which is heavier: a Fiat Panda or
Giant Haystacks? Can I get from Letchworth to Wembley
in a shopping trolley without someone dropping a piano
on my head? Can you teach a dog to drive a Lamborghini?
On it goes.

√√√ √
*Great
ideas,
actually!!!*

Lassie in a Lambo

On the days we shoot in the studio I have to
entertain the sweaty bald blokes and the felonious
lesbians without any back-up, and the strain is
beginning to tell. I've given Amil the shortlist of
replacements and he just laughed and handed me one he'd
drawn up.

'You've got to cast against type, Jez,' he says, his little brown eyes twinkling.

His list includes none of my preferred names, and the first name I come to is Kirsty Wark.

'For fuck's sake, Amil, she's Scotch!'

'So am I,' Amil says, as if this is the most reasonable thing in the world.

'Really? Well, but you're not proper Scotch. It's not like you're ginger and ugly and everything. And who's this? Kate Humble?'

'Her paternal grandfather was a test pilot. He tested the Hawker Tempest.'

'But she's a veganist! No one will want to see a veganist in a short skirt getting out of a car! And Nana Mous-fucking-kouri?'

On it goes; one dreary baggy-breasted old boiler after the other until we get to Janet Street-Porter and then I thank the lord I am a smoker and have a cigarette lighter to hand. 'I'd rather ask Ozzy Osbourne to flatten my purple-wurple with a two-pound lump hammer than be in a room with Janet Street Bloody Porter,' I start.

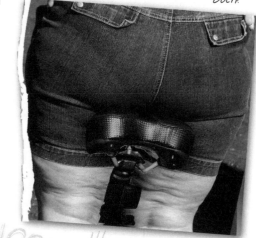

✓✓✓ ✓
Ouch!

'Do you hear me? I'd rather cycle from here to John O'cocking Groats behind Fearne Felch or whatever her name is - naked - on a tandem - with a broken saddle, and no Vaseline.'

Amil starts and then beams at me.

NOOo₀..!!!

137

'Valerie Choade! You genius Jeremy! Yes! That is exactly who we shall ask.

Valerie Choade is this country's answer to Adolf Hitler, a TV chat show hostess with a crêpey cleavage and a gastric band long since gone bust. Her career turtled after she was caught shop-lifting Preparation H from Morrisons, and ever since she's been lying at home on her chaise-longue, eating Philadelphia dippers and shouting at her new husband while he hoovers the carpet wearing nothing but a French maid's outfit. She is the very worst person in the world.

I am about to hit Amil but just then the fire alarm goes off and we're soaked by the sprinklers.

'And I bet she'll be free for the Bond-off,' he adds.

WEDNESDAY 11TH AUGUST

The stars racing for world peace this week are two great big black blokes with shaved heads from somewhere south of the Sahara. One is a member of some organization called the Lord's Resistance Army, the other the President of Congo. Each of them wears aviator sunglasses, olive combat shirts and their trousers tucked into combat boots and they sit on the sofa with their legs apart. Whenever I ask them questions they just laugh great deep chocolatey laughs and the only way I can tell them apart is that one of

The President of the Congo

them has more gold teeth than the other. It turns out they are brothers.

'Tell me Jeremy,' one of them says, 'where did you get your watch?'

'Can you get me the personal telephone number of Dawn French?' the other asks.

Then they race around the track in their cars and one of them wins and they shake hands and agree some sort of cease-fire and we bring peace to millions of women and children and for once even George Monbiot can't complain.

FRIDAY 20TH AUGUST

So here we are. Bond-Off minus one. The day before the day we've all been waiting for.

Except, of course, that I can't even begin to enjoy it.

You see, I have to sit next to Valerie Choade on the flight to Frankfurt.

She flumps down next to me with a waft of something almost as nasty as Joop! and starts telling me about the magazine she's brought, called *Allrite*?

'I was in the supermarket doing the lottery when I saw this headline: "Devil Dog

ripped off my arm and ate it!"
And I thought, oooh, I've got
two Westies and they wouldn't
dream of hurting anyone, but
then I thought to myself, well
would they? I mean you never can be
too careful with animals, can you? I mean neither of my
Westies are like the dog that bit the woman who wrote
the article. I mean, the dog that bit her was 13 stone!
Can you believe that? And his name was Diesel!'

I can't think of a thing to say.

'A Rottweiler, he was. Mmm. Yes.'

She turns back to her magazine, I turn to the window
and for a moment I miss Rammond. All right he does smell
of Joop! and he is incredibly annoying and he does say
'as you do' all the time, but at least he sticks to his
own seat.

'It's got everything in it,' I hear her going on.
'Look. There's fashion, and tips, and a psychic tarot, and
they pay you for your photos if you send them in and
there's health and a page of no-nonsense advice from
Denise who fronts *This Morning* on ITV, I think it is, and
then there's stuff about the telly and your holidays.'

Amil, Natasha and the crew are in economy and I can
hear them all having quite a good time.

'And even, look! - recipes. Ooh. Sausages and
colcannon. Cabbage and cheese pasta. Easy chilli beef,
is it? Chicken liver pasta, spaghetti carbonara, fishfinger
pie. I like the sound of that, don't you?'

Oooooh!!! At the airport we're met by Sabine, who has driven
around the Nürburgring eleventy million times in her
taxi, and to whom I once, in those far off happy days,

offered Rammond's job. Valerie barrels up to her and
starts talking about how they are women together and
that sort of thing, and again the magazine comes out and
Sabine is unusually respectful, perhaps because Valerie
looks so much like the German Chancellor Helmut Kohl, or
do I mean Angela Merkin?

Anyway, we all pile into a fleet of taxis and off we
go to the Nürburgring.

We've taken the precaution of separating most of
the Bonds so that there's no trouble: Connery is
flying in tomorrow for the day only, 'for tax reasons';
Moore is staying in a private wing of the Kemperhof
Hospital in Koblenz; Craig is staying in the Hotel
Wilhelmshöhe; Brosnan and Lazenby in a twin room at a
nearby guesthouse; and we've given Dalton a 'superior
class' pitch at the Camping am Nürburgring, the website
of which promises 'Natur & Komfort', as well as something
called 'Bombenstimmung', which doesn't need a lot of
imagination to understand as a condition that might be
painful, but is easily avoided with the application of a
good thick lube.

Bombenstimmung!!! Natur UND Komfort

The crew are staying at yet another hotel while
Valerie and I are in the Gästehaus Dietrich, which
I understand to be a romantic hideaway in the Eifel
Mountains.

We arrive at the garage and there are the cars,
lined up, ready and waiting, and at this point not even
thoughts of Valerie Choade can keep my erection under
control.

The Aston Martin DB5 is there in all its pant-
soiling beauty. This one is an original, borrowed from
some auto-eroticist's collection in Holland, and it's
the one Connery will use, even though we can't afford
the insurance. Next to it is a Lotus S1, badly painted
yellow, which we'll give to Roger Moore. He's on so many
painkillers after his 'accident' that he won't even
realize that the car won't start, because of course they
never do.

Lazenby's car is the biggest: a Mercury Cougar from
1969, and it is a thing of lavish, brash beauty, as

Post-coital glow!

direct as the DB5 is restrained. Old but funky, like Joan
Collins in fishnets.

Next to it is Brosnan's choice: a BMW 7 series, a
tremendously anonymous-looking car, designed on the lines
of a chairman's open sandwich, and with just the same
appeal.

Daniel Craig is in a tan-coloured Kia Picanto. We
thought long and hard about this one and then, having
spanked our budget on the BMW, we just gave him the
cheapest we could find at the Eurorentals.

Dalton is driving his car straight to his superior
pitch at the campsite tonight. It really is his car.
A Nissan Almera, which I won't allow him to bring over
until tomorrow. I flinch when I see an Almera. I flinch in
the same way I'd flinch if a naked Johnny Vegas was about √√√√√
to sit on my face and tell me that he loved me. *must use on BottomGear!!!*

'So,' Amil says, 'we'll meet all the Bonds here at
eight tomorrow morning, people, and then we'll head to
the track to set things up and get set for the arrival.
So get an early night.'

Valerie says something about needing her beauty sleep,
but when we get to the Gästehaus
Dietrich there has been some mix-up
and we are sharing a room, just as I
would have with Rammond.

'Well, this is awkward,' she says
as we both get caught in the doorway
of the room, tummy to tummy. She is
very small from top to bottom. The
room is peach coloured and smells of pot-pourri. Thank
God there are twin beds, I think.

Then I open the complimentary bottle of champagne-

143

style substance and pour two flutes. I drink mine down,
refill it, hand hers to her. Our fingers touch. Oh my God.
I don't know where to look. I drain my glass. In the
fridge are some peanuts and another bottle of the fizzy
wine. I eat them and then drink most of that...

Now Valerie is unpacking her suitcase, hanging up
her pants suits, taking underwear out of her case and
putting it in drawers and what's wrong with me? All I
can think of is...

Later I find I've pushed the beds together.

'You're nothing like how I imagined you'd be,' she's
saying. 'You give out this really macho air, don't you
Jemmy, but there's a really sensitive side to you, isn't
there?'

I nod my head. Even my hair feels heavy.

Later on I find I've opened another bottle...

'Come here, you,' I hear myself saying.

And she does.

SATURDAY 21ST AUGUST

'Closed? The fucking Nürburgring's *closed*?'

Amil is sitting on the end of my bed shouting into
his iPhone.

I look at my outsize Italian football manager's
watch. It is 7.30.

I am stiff and sore and even my hair is crisp.

'Did you hear that, Jeremy? The Bonds are going to be
here in five fucking minutes and we've got no racetrack!
What the hell are we going to do?'

I don't care about the Bonds. I only care that I
smell of something worse than Joop! and I have a bastard
of a headache behind the eyes.

What the f*@k

Errr...

have I done?!!

Through the bathroom door the bog flushes.

Amil stares at me, his mouth open.

'What have you DONE?' he whispers.

Valerie emerges wearing only a towel and the complimentary shower cap.

'Oh hello, Amil!' she says, all smiles. She is apricot coloured.

Amil backs out of the room.

'I'll see you at the garage in twenty minutes,' he says.

'See you,' she says as if this is all perfectly normal and then she starts humming as she dresses, pulling on a pair of pants the size of an ordinary person's pillow case. I turn and bury my face in the sheets.

What have I done?

Valerie hums as she packs and in the taxi makes small talk to the driver.

I am silent until we get there.

'So what the fuck are we going to do?'

Amil has pulled all his hair out and is moving on to the girlchild, whose responsibility it was to make sure the Nürburgring was open today. She is weeping in the corner. Natasha looks pale.

Then there is the sound of a small Japanese car pulling up outside.

One of the crew pokes his head in.

'Timothy Dalton's here!'

Amil gulps.

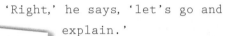

'Right,' he says, 'let's go and explain.'

Timothy Dalton is looking less constipated than usual, like a fresh-faced log.

Amil is all over him.

'Timothy! Timothy Timothy Timothy! How was your night?'

'Not bad,' Timothy Dalton says. 'Nice little campsite. Lovely facilities. Thanks for steering me in that direction.'

We all stare at him as he goes on about the shower block and the outdoor table-tennis tables and the crazy golf course.

'It's terrific,' he says. 'Modelled on world landmarks, you know, so you've got the Statue of Liberty, the Taj Mahal, the Leaning Tower of Pisa, and so on. I played two rounds last night when I got in and came in on 67.'

Now this is golfosexualism in its most extreme form. It is the golfing equivalent of having yourself pinned out on Hampstead Heath with croquet hoops in the hope that someone wearing a gimp mask will come along and defecate on you, but if you've been paying attention to what has gone before, you'll know what is just about to happen now.

SEXUAL PERVERSIONS:
THE SHORTLIST

Golfosexualism

Envirosexualism

Ramblism

Cyclism

Ornitholojizzum

Vegetablism

'Wait a minute,' I say. 'If we can't sort out who is the best Bond by racing around the Nürburgring, what about a game of crazy golf?'

Timothy Dalton is up for it.

Once again Natasha is on the phone, redirecting the stars in our cars from racetrack to campsite.

Then we get in the Bond cars - except the Lotus that won't start - and we drive to the campsite. I take the DB5, Valerie the Picanto. She gets lost after the first left turn.

Now, I've never been to a campsite. I have no idea what to expect. What I find there not only repels me, but bewilders me. Why would people pay money to sleep in tents in a car park? And why are the women so incredibly ugly? They look like organic vegetables. Yes, yes, organic vegetables may taste better than supermarket vegetables but I don't want to taste these people, I want them to parade decoratively before me like Rachel Weisz on her knees or Cameron Diaz on all fours. Yet this seems to be a nest of leather-skinned fresh-airists and everything is so ugly I doubt we can actually film here. The cameras simply won't record it.

Timothy Dalton is showing us what he calls the campsite facilities when Brosnan and Lazenby show up in a taxi.

Brosnan is an Irishman pretending to be an American, while Lazenby is an Australian pretending to be an Australian. It makes no sense but it hardly matters. Both are dressed in the clothes that golfists usually wear and they unload great big bags full of golf bats from the back of the taxi. They are taking it very seriously.

They shake hands with Timothy Dalton, and start to discuss their pensions and their various ailments before showing one another photos of their grandchildren.

Then Craig turns up in a jeep, wearing smart but casual clothes and pair of Benelux clogs. His skin looks like it is made from the same stuff they used for Action Man's diving suit back in the 1970, and he is so bulky and padded out it looks as if he's swallowed the tube.

Timothy Dalton is only interested in Lazenby's post-Bond career:

'So did you get to pork Sylvia Kristel in *Emmanuelle in Space*?'

6' 5"
6' 0"
5' 5"
5' 0"
4' 5"
4' 0"
3' 5"
3' 0"

RAMMOND

'Ah, actually, I wasn't in that one. I did *Secret*, *Paris*, *Revenge* and *Forever*, but not *Space*. I wanted to do *Emmanuelle versus Dracula*, but I had commitments elsewhere.'

Lazenby is the tallest by about a head. He is nearly a decent height, but the others are pathetically tiny. Like toys. Like Rammond.

I should be writing thrillers!

There is the whumping of rotorblades as Connery's helicopter fills the sky above our heads. It touches down among the tents, sending them flying in every direction.

Amil signals to get the cameraman on me, and I know I have to clutch my sides laughing.

Then Connery leaps out, nimble and sprightly, but I can't help noticing that in his golf slacks and tank top, he looks not unlike Jimmy Tarbuck - when he was alive of course (actually, is he alive? - he might be - anyway, you get my point) - and if he'd dipped his chin in silver paint. The helicopter takes off behind and Connery advances towards us in a cloud of dust, so small he does not feel the need to duck the rotor blades.

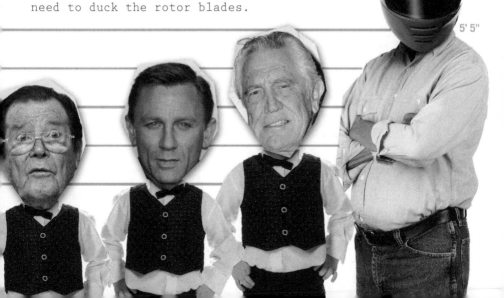

'Ah, the other fellows,' he says, when the noise has died down. He is almost as small as Rammond and is, I have to say, a bit of a disappointment. He shakes their hands and they are all too shy to look at him.

Timothy Dalton has to introduce himself twice.

'Where's that dopey wee bastard, Moore?' Connery asks.

He obviously toned his Scotch accent down to play Bond, but now here it is, almost incomprehensible, even though he hasn't been to Scotland for more than twenty years.

'I suppose you're talking about me?'

It is Roger Moore, wearing a hospital gown and sitting in an electric wheelchair, one eyebrow now permanently raised since the emergency operation. He has zipped his way through the crowds of people struggling to their feet after the chopper blew away their tents.

When Valerie finally pulls up in the Kia Picanto she curtseys to the Bonds and they move in on her, each one trying to out-do the other with old-world charm. Soon she is walking towards the odd little patch of miniature buildings which I presume is the golf course with Connery on one arm, Moore zipping along in his wheelchair on the other.

Moore and Connery

Connery is trying to talk over Moore, and he's really putting on the voice now.

'Yesh. Cubby told me he thought my performance in *Thunderball*, was it? Yesh.

you would!

Miss Moneypenny, can I trouble you for some viagra?

Thunderball. He said that was the best Bond performance he'd ever seen.'

'Did you ever, you know? With Moneypenny?'

This is from Moore. It takes Connery back. He hesitates.

'Ah. No. Sir Roger. Not with Missh Moneypenny. I had too much reshpect for her as an actress, and as a woman.'

'Oh me too, but... '

Sir Roger tries to raise his eyebrow, but after I squashed him with my car it's been stitched on funny, as if by someone who makes his own shoes, so no one knows what he means.

Through all this Valerie has not stopped talking about *Allrite?* magazine.

'You'd love it, Sir Roger! It's just like you!'

'Just like me, Valerie?'

'Oh yes, it's cheeky,' she says. 'It's irreverent and fun, too, full of stories, puzzles, irresistible fashion bargains, bonuses and surprises.'

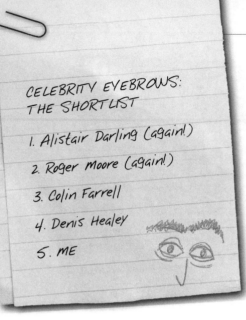

CELEBRITY EYEBROWS:
THE SHORTLIST

1. Alistair Darling (again!)

2. Roger Moore (again!)

3. Colin Farrell

4. Denis Healey

5. ME

'How's your wife, Sir Roger?' Connery asks over her.

'The Danish model and billionairess?'

'Yesh.'

I interrupt to ask if either of them watch *BottomGear*. Moore won't speak to me of course after our run-in up in Crans-Montana. Sir Sean raises his eyebrows - suspiciously black, I can't help thinking, and wondering if the curtains match before I stop myself and realize what I am doing - and shakes his head.

'No,' he says.

I laugh as if they're both joking.

Now all the Bonds are together, lining up for their photo in front of the crazy golf course, and it is a frankly disturbing sight. Not even Valerie can think of what to say as they stand - or sit, in Sir Roger's case - in their tank tops and tartan trousers holding their golf rackets as if they mean business.

'Gentlemen,' I say, 'take your sticks and let the game begin.'

Watching grown men knock a little ball around a huge field is one thing, but watching them do it around a miniaturized set of world landmarks makes even less sense. Pretty soon I want to join in. I rent a mallet from the boy in the booth and begin on the first hole, trailing behind Craig, who wears his title of junior Bond with a mixture of pride and shame.

The first is a twenty-five-foot straight hit that ends with a sharp rise through a two-foot Arc de Triomphe, under which the hole is hidden. I tap the ball and it wings along the red painted concrete, creeps up the rise, goes through the legs of the Arc and plock into the hole.

I am astonished. It is the single greatest sporting moment of my life.

You see I have never been very good at anything. The list of things I can actually do is very very short. Spell, yes, I can do that. Come up with arresting imagery, ditto, once in a while anyway. Drive a car, I suppose, though of course not very well. What I've never been able to do is hit a ball with a stick or my foot. Perhaps it comes of having a face like a gonad? It means I have innate sympathy for the ball. That is what James always says.

Craig is watching my shot though, as is Valerie, who coos.

'Nice shot, Jeremy,' Craig says through a clenched jaw, then, in an aside: 'Listen, there's something I wanted to talk to you about.'

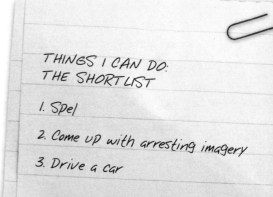

THINGS I CAN DO: THE SHORTLIST

1. Spel

2. Come up with arresting imagery

3. Drive a car

He looks around rubberly.

Valerie wanders off to get a burger.

'I want to win this,' he says.

'I'm sure you do,' I reply. In truth all I can think of is the sound that ball made as it rattled into the hole.

'I'm prepared to offer anything you like for your help.'

'Well...'

'No, look. Anything. I know you don't need money or a car, but what about women?'

'Women?'

'Men, then?'

'No, no, no.'

I find I am whispering. Valerie is coming back with her burger. Craig glances at her and then back at me, and his eyes widen as if he has finally worked something out.

'I'm sorry,' he says, 'I didn't realize...'

'No, no, no, no! I'm not with her!' I scream.

Valerie stops. She drops her burger and turns and half runs, half walks away.

Daniel Craig looks at me and clenches his jaw for a moment.

He plays his shot. The ball pings off Big Ben and rolls back to his feet.

'What will it take?' he asks. 'I've got Olga Kurylenko's number, you know? I could give it to you. Now. I have it here.'

He passes me a piece of paper. At that moment Connery hits Moore with his golf ball. An accident? I think not.

Moore retaliates by running his wheelchair over

Connery's foot. Connery hits him again. Moore calls Connery a 'turd-burglar'.

Amil is trying to keep the peace.

'Where's Valerie?' he shouts.

She is weeping behind a tree.

Meanwhile: 'So you were in *Emmanuelle's Perfume*, too, right?'

It is Timothy Dalton, still on at George Lazenby about his post-Bond acting career. Lazenby is running out of patience. He chips his ball over a model of the Sphinx and it bounces off a pyramid and out onto the rough Eurograss.

'Oh, cock,' he says and he turns to Natasha.

'Young lady, he spoke to me just as I was making my approach. I think I should be allowed to take that shot again.'

'Oh, fuck off, you big Kiwi poof!'

This is from Brosnan, who is only a stroke ahead of Lazenby. He pushes Lazenby, who turns and raises his bat.

'I'm Australian, you know, and I'm not gay.'

'Yeah right, course you are.'

Brosnan was always a wit. Lazenby, elderly, grey haired, retired underwear model, takes a step towards him. Brosnan takes off, running with his

Fuck off, you big Kiwi poof!

arms pumping as if he were a founder member of the Village People at a New York bath house.

'He always was a coward,' says Lazenby.

'It's only a game,' Timothy Dalton says, trying to be all reasonable.

'And you can fuck off too, you, whoever you are.'

In the silence that follows Connery takes the opportunity to tip Moore out of the chair. He lands in a welter of callipers and casts.

'That's for Miss Moneypenny, ya daft wee shite!' Connery shouts, all his Bond smoothness gone.

Moore scrabbles in the dust on his back like a tan-coloured beetle. He wriggles behind a two foot model of the Acropolis and I recall that scene in *Live and Let Die* when he wriggled a lot.

'We did it doggy style, you know!' Moore pipes up from behind his hide-out.

'Where is that wee fucker?' shouts Connery. 'Ahm goin' ta kill him.'

But from the cover of the acropolis, Moore manipulates the control pad of his electric wheelchair, and he sends it zipping between two pyramids to crash into Connery's frankly dodgy-looking legs.

'Not the sort of delivery you were expecting, eh, Mr Milky?' he shouts.

Connery buckles and staggers over towards Moore, only before he gets there, he trips over the Colosseum, falling heavily on Moore. Moore screams. It is higher pitched than I would expect, and I wonder if perhaps my running him down in Crans-Montana has had any adverse affect in his trouser department?

Moore and Connery grapple like a couple of schoolgirls
until Moore's nurse, a Korean dwarf with a speech
impediment, separates them with a series of swift karate-
style blows.

Both are panting heavily.

Moore gestures at his chair.

'You expect me to walk?'

Connery screams and throws himself back into the fight.

Behind them I notice that Craig has jumped two holes
and is shaping up to pot the winner. Beyond *him*, Valerie
is still weeping. I look at the number Craig has given
me. Who *is* Olga Kurylenko, I wonder.

THURSDAY 26TH AUGUST

So with a little help from me, Daniel Craig is the best
James Bond.

Not that this has gone down well with everyone. Sean
Connery has retired to the Cayman Islands
and is refusing to visit either
Europe or his beloved Scotland to
pay any taxes ever again. When
this is announced the BBC call me
to ask not for a reaction, but whether
I will fill Connery's slot on their new family
history show: *Hi there, Ancestors!*.

'I've already done *Who Do you Think You
Are?*' I say.

'Yes. But we've also been doing some
research? And we've found something that
is really like kind of amazing?'

'Really? What?'

'Well, we'd only be willing to tell

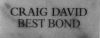

CRAIG DAVID
BEST BOND

A TREE WITH A FAT GIRL BEHIND IT
- AND SHE'S EATING A BUN

you if you agreed to be filmed being told,
so that you don't have to act surprised
later on? Should you agree to do the
show?'

When I tell Zafira afterwards she tells me
I must do it, and I feel so guilty about my
night with Valerie that I agree. 'Why not?'
I say.

'Well, we had Mr Connery down for
tomorrow? While he was in Europe? Would
you be free then?'

'Er. All right.'

To be honest I don't care much about
it because the most exciting thing in the world is
happening at home. And no, I don't mean Keira Knightley
doing the limbo wearing nothing but a thong and a
Guardsman's busby. I mean that I am having a crazy golf
course built in the rose garden.

It is going to be made of felt on a concrete base,
with kerbstones on the borders, and the designer has
created models of my favourite cars and placed them so
that I have to clip the ball through their open doors,
say, in the case of the Porsche Carrera GT, or under
their wheels with the Aston Martin V8 Vantage. There are
nine holes and the work should be done by the weekend.

Now that I have discovered a game I'm good at, I can't
wait to get out there. I have bought a pair of loud
checked trousers and a Pringle sweater and three bagfuls
of brushed titanium bats.

FRIDAY 27TH AUGUST

The most extraordinary day of my life.

I drive the Range Rover up to the BBC again. It feels
strange not to be seeing Amil, but he and Natasha are
seeing the Director General about Valerie. He hasn't
seen the rushes of the Bond-off, but it's pretty obvious
that Valerie isn't up to the job. The chemistry is all
wrong. During the James Bonds' fight she ate a burger
and wept behind a tree, which made for good television,
but only if it is the sort you watch through your fingers
from behind the sofa.

The *Hi there, Ancestors!* production office is a
cupboard on the backstairs compared to *BottomGear*'s
office and the producer - Rebecca something - bustles
about the place in a cardigan. She looks like one
of those little birds that Italians enjoy shooting.
Sparrows? Finches?

'Do you want to put something smarter on?' she asks.

I am wearing my best pair of blue jeans and a shirt.

'No,' I say.

Anyway, she's tremendously excited about something, but
she refuses to tell me what it is. So we head eastwards
through London in the back of a cab, a cameraman filming
me as we pass the Houses of Parliament and Kings
Cross and so on. All the way she asks questions about
my parents and brothers and sisters. It turns out
we're heading towards the Family Records Centre in
Clerkenwell.

They've set aside a room for us. On a large table is
a pile of registers marked with post-it notes. After
last week this hardly seems like television at all. I
sit down and they push the register across the table to

me. I see my mother's name and then my father's and mine and I think well, so what?

Then I see what Rebecca is pointing too.

This is not a register of births.

This is a register of adoptions.

meet the Klaxons

'I'm adopted?'

'Yes.'

This takes a moment to sink in, of course.

'So my real parents?'

'Are alive. They live with your brother.'

'My brother!'

'Your twin brother.'

I am stunned.

Rebecca is nodding and smiling.

'Would you like to meet him?' she asks.

This is all a bit sudden, I think, but I can't say no, can I?

Then they film me getting back in the cab and all I can think of is to wonder what car he drives. Please don't let it be a Peugeot, I am thinking. Please don't let it be anything by Hyundai!

The cab pulls up at the Groucho Club where another cameraman is waiting to film me getting out.

The Groucho Club.

I know what you're thinking. It is easy to groan about the Groucho Club, but just as France is a good place to keep the French, the Groucho Club is a good place to keep North London mediarasts.

√√√
Piss off,
Ventob!!

160

Its shiny bar top keeps their strangely bespectacled eyes focused, its thick glass and wood doors keep them corralled, its flat surfaces above the toilets keep them up all night, inspiring them to genius programming ideas such as *Minipops, Through the Keyhole, Heil Honey I'm Home!* and *Eldorado*.

Having said that, just like France, it's best to pass through the Groucho Club on your way to other, better things. In fact, were I not here to meet a long-lost relative - and a twin at that - I'd rather drink ✓✓✓ Susan Boyle's bathwater than roll my sleeves up and order a bottle of foreign lager-style drink at the Groucho bar.

But today I am not here for the scenery. Today I AM here to meet my long-lost relative, and a twin at that.

Julian.

The receptionist - no thank you very much, madam, not today at any rate - points me in the right direction. Through the double doors and into one of the meeting rooms.

What were they thinking?

And there he is.

Well, I assume it's him since there is no one else in the room and when he sees me he stands up, looking uncertain.

What can I say about him?

He looks just like me.

Just like me, that is, if I were a couple of stone lighter. Just like me, that is, if I had a face that didn't resemble a shaved testicle, and just like me, indeed, if my hair was cut by someone who wasn't registered to claim Blind Person's Allowance. He would have dressed exactly like me, too, had he been wearing clothes made for someone else by a butcher who had heard of clothes, but had never actually seen them on.

But he wasn't.

He was wearing a suit and open-necked shirt, both of which seemed to fit him rather well and a pair of shoes that seemed to have been made for him. His hair was cut shorter than mine and wasn't so - is sporadic the right word here? Probably. Nor had his face the rough droop of a plucked and plucked scrotum.

Julian: gay AND French

When faced with this sort of thing I usually opt for bluster, and ask the waiter to bring me something, or insult a nearby Korean, or talk about a late 1970s Dutch prog rock band, but faced with my handsome, well-groomed, clearly very intelligent twin brother there was only one thing I could say.

'But you're gay!'

'Et en plus, je suis français!'

SUNDAY 29TH AUGUST

News of the fight at the Bond-off has been all over the newspapers after Amil leaked a taster of the action on Youbookfacetube or whatever it is called, and there has been a hell of a fuss about the discovery of Julian, so when a *Sunday Times* reporter rings in the morning I assume he's after a quote on either.

In the event it is neither.

BONDS TRADE BLOWS IN CRAZY GOLF COURSE BUST-UP!

Zafira has taken the horses down to compete in some three-day event gymkhana-style thing and I'm playing *Call of Duty Modern Warfare 2*, on single-player mode, and I'm using a sniper rifle and a missile launcher to protect the Washington evacuation zone from the Russians.

'Thanks for talking to me, Jez,' the reporter starts, 'I just wonder if you can confirm or deny the rumour that you and Valerie Choade spent the night with one another while you were in Nürburg?'

My blood freezes and I tell him no comment and hang up.

I can hear my hair curling at the thought of the headlines.

I am on the point of ringing my manager when I recall that she is also my wife.

Who can I talk to? With James in Turkey and Rammond away in Morocco filming *Monster Blast Canteen As You Do* there is no one left to turn to.

I collapse in the chair again.

Call of Duty is still running on the screen and I dimly see that I have completed my objectives and now there follows a cut-scene in which the hoary old SAS

Captain Price, now freed from the Gulag, is on the horn - as he would say - to General Shepherd.

'You wanna put out an oil fire, sir?' he asks rhetorically, 'you set off a bigger explosion right next to it. Sucks away the oxygen. Snuffs the flame.'

It is then that it hits me.

Price is right. Not just about setting off the Submarine-Launched Ballistic Missile to explode over the US, but about Valerie. The news of our night together is the oil fire. I need a bigger explosion to snuff it out.

Captain John Price does not seem to me to be a conventionally happy man, I admit, and I wouldn't ordinarily think of taking careers advice from a character in a video game, but, as he would say, let's do this.

But how? And what?

And now coincidence really plays its part, for there on the coffee table next to me, marked by a wine ring, is one of Zafira's gossip magazines. Not *Allrite?*, I shudder with relief, but *Hello!* and there, on the front page, is a beautiful young woman with an unpronounceable name returning to Ukraine to help foster orphan goats or gay donkeys. Anyway, blah blah blah.

You would, that is all I am saying, and you'd take your time doing it. And then I have it.

CAR CHASES: THE SHORTLIST

1. Ben Hur
2. Dr Zhivago
3. The French Connection
4. Bullitt
5. BottomGear
6. Bergerac (episodes 1-92)

I reach for the phone and dial a number written on a piece of paper.

'Hello,' says a bored Eastern European voice.

'Hello, Olga.'

WEDNESDAY 1ST SEPTEMBER

Thank God it was *The Sunday Times* and not *The Times* who found out about my night with Valerie Choade, otherwise it'd be all over the shop by now, like the rash in a cheap hooker's pants.

Shades of Chandler?

Instead I've three days to set off my 'bigger explosion'.

My theory, backed up by Captain Price, is that Zafira will never believe anything about me and Olga Kuthingy, since the pouting Ukrainian probably wouldn't want to shack up with a fat middle-aged bald bloke with a dodgy hip, however charming and rich he may be. If the newspapers think there's even a chance of it, though, that's the story they'll print, because they'll be able to splash huge pictures of Olga on their front pages.

Anyway there is not much I can do about it today though because today I'm back at the track again with Kim Jong-Il (not to be confused with Kim Yong-il, Kim Jong-pil, or even Kim Jong-Il, the athlete) and a man called Lee Mung Bean, who is, we are told, the president of a place called South Korea. They are here today to race around the track to decide the fate of that self-same Korea and all its millions of little Koreans, and presumably their dogs too.

Now, unlike most things Korean - by which I mean their cars and those dogs again (after they have been slathered in tomato sauce) - you can actually tell

Lee Mung Bean

the difference between King Kong-Il and Mung-Bean-Ill. You see, one of them looks like a damaged chick in glasses wearing army surplus clothes made for someone else, while the other looks like a bank clerk.

I have no idea which one rules which country, but I know which one looks like more fun.

Anyway, Amil is walking on eggshells.

'Please don't make any more dog-eating jokes, Jeremy,' he says, 'and for the love of all that is holy, no Chinese impressions?'

'Why not?' I ask.

'Well, for one neither is Chinese, and for two both have nuclear weapons.'

I look at them again in a whole new light now. And sure enough I can see a little flunky following behind each one of them. He's carrying a briefcase which I had thought held their dog sandwiches, but now understand might be the Big Red Button. Well, not THE Big Red Button. That is, as I discovered the other night, located somewhere in Valerie Choade's pants.

So today they are going to race around the track in two Animedic vans, the sort dog wardens use to round up strays. At first Amil said no, on the grounds that the choice of vehicle could only encourage me to make even more dog jokes. And of course he was right.

FRIDAY 3RD SEPTEMBER

Work on the crazy golf course has finished and the men in
overalls are putting the finishing touches to the cars,
each one made of cement, and each one no bigger than
two foot two inches.

Hole number one is a gentle opener that leads to
the Lamborghini Gallardo Spyder. After this there's
a long rise up to the Aston Martin V8 Vantage.
You have to get this one just right because if
you don't hit the ball so that it just creeps
over the crest of the hill, it comes rolling all
the way back past the tee. Then there's the BMW
M5, which is stepped and - unless you can chip it
- a par four, followed immediately by a nasty-looking
dogleg at the VW Phaeton. On it goes. There is a vicious
hole at the Rolls-Royce Phantom, but my favourite is the
Audi RS4 coupe, where you have to chip the ball into the
driver's footwell, from where it rolls out of the exhaust
and, if you are lucky, into the hole.

I'd be out there now if it weren't that I have a date
with Olga tonight.

I've told Zafira that I'm off up to London to see the
Director General to get Rammond reinstated on *BottomGear*,
but in fact I'm meeting Olga in a place called Boujis. I
have no idea what it will be like.

I put on my best jeans and shirt, making sure I turn
the sleeves up a notch so that my monkey wrists are on
show, along with my new watch. Then I slip on Lancia-
branded driving shoes. I look at myself in the mirror.

Should I have plastic surgery?

On balance, probably not.

Right, here goes. Wish me luck.

A COOKED DOG

SATURDAY 4TH SEPTEMBER

Wake up in a prison cell feeling as if Godzilla has shat in my brain.

Very patchy memories of night before. I remember arriving at this Boujis place having already had five tins of Foster's on the way up. Felt very gassy. Met the photographer from *The Sunday Times* outside, then went in and found Olga.

The club itself is stuffed with orange-faced chavs from Basildon and even if I wasn't carrying the page torn from Zafira's *Hello!* I'd have recognized Olga among them.

Agonizingly beautiful, of course, like an Enzo Ferrari, only without the redness, or the thick black rubber tyres, or, come to that, the exhaust pipes.

At first things were a bit awkward. I kept burping and she hadn't ever owned a car and all she ever said was 'what?' After a few vodkas though, things warmed up. She can drink like any Latvian and when we went on to the dance floor a space opened up around us as we sort of shrugged along to the music and it was all going really well and out of the corner of my eye I could see the photographer snapping away.

After our dance my shirt is wringing wet and I down yet more vodka. Then I get mixed up between Lithuania or Ukraine or whichever it is Olga comes from, and I ask her if she knows my friend Nikolai whom I met on holiday a few years ago and even though she doesn't, because he's Albanian not from Slivovitz or wherever it is she comes from. Anyway I start on about last year's holiday, when we took his boat out on the Adriatic fishing trip.

It doesn't sound an interesting story, I know, but if

my wife doesn't understand me and the TA wouldn't have me

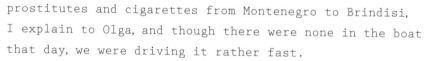

you're thinking a rod and reel and endless hours reading pornographic magazines on the banks of the reservoir while you're waiting for a tench to nibble, think again.

You see, in Albania they do things somewhat differently.

Nikolai makes a living smuggling underage prostitutes and cigarettes from Montenegro to Brindisi, I explain to Olga, and though there were none in the boat that day, we were driving it rather fast.

In fact we were doing about forty knots.

So how do you catch a fish doing that sort of speed?

Easy. Easy, that is, if you have a machine gun.

Luckily my friend Nikolai has quite a few of them in his line of business and so, thanks to Mr Heckler and Mr Koch, we pass the afternoon happily machine-gunning dolphins.

√√
Up yours,
Bill Oddie!!

I tell her I'll show her the photos, if she wants?

She seems unimpressed.

But that doesn't matter. The photographer is taking hundreds of sneaky shots and already I can see tomorrow's headlines: Motor Mouth Klaxon Takes a New Model for a Spin, or something.

I drink more vodka and then lean in for a peck on the lips.

Olga shrinks back but she is too late!

We touched!

'Don't you fucking dare do that again!' she spits, but the photographer gives me the thumbs up. Then he signals he needs more.

Hmmm.

Olga is about to leave.

'Do you know that song "Night Moves"?' I ask.

'"Night Moves"?' she says. 'What is "Night Moves"?'

'A song,' I say. And then I start singing, 'Tight Pants, Points, hardly renowned, she was a black haired beauty with big dark eyes, And points of her own sitting way up high, way up firm and high.'

You see, I am already wondering how I can touch her breasts, and that's when it happens.

The Shaved Chimp makes his appearance.

Piers bloody Morgan.

Up he comes with his eyeballs and capped teeth glowing in the weird blue light and he looks like one of those monster-fish hybrids you find at the bottom of the Mariana Trench. His head is like a summer fruit and just about as full of brains, though sadly not so soft, as I discovered to my cost a few years ago when I hit it and broke a finger.

I introduce them and because he has been on some crap talent-spotting show in the US, and may know Simon Cowell, I can see instantly that if I don't do something fast, my 'bigger explosion' will splutter and die.

Now, I know I've broken my finger fighting Morgan before, but that is no bar to me doing it again.

As he is leaning in telling Olga about his balcony and the matching table and chairs, and his new Porsche, and his handmade suits and how much that cunt Cowell owes his success to him, I take a swing.

The thinking man's monkey (right)

SUNDAY 5TH SEPTEMBER

Amil comes to collect me from the police station, greeting me as you would a Nigerian leper. I can't look him in the eye either, not because I'm ashamed of myself, but because it turns out he drives an old Volkswagen Passat. In the back are three car seats and the glove compartment is stuffed with scratched Harry Potter audio book CDs.

I have been drinking confiscated rum and coke with the boys in blue for the best part of two days and need a bath like a Polish whore after the Red Army's come knocking. I remember I am expecting Julian for lunch at my house at one o'clock.

The worse thing is that he is bringing his partner.

Julian - or Jules as he likes to be called - is going
to fill me in on his life, from the moment he was given
up for adoption and taken to Paris, the discovery that
he is gay, to the moment he was told we were twins.

Amil drives me to Chipping Norton and drops me at my
front door.

Zafira is away with the horses again, competing in
another gymkhana, and the papers lie uncollected on the
doorstep. *The Sunday Times* has me on the front page
looking drunken but victorious at least, and on page five
there are pictures of the fight, including the regulars
(and Prince Harry) gathered around in a ring shouting
'Fight! Fight!' as the Shaved Chimp and I trade blows.

Luckily there is no sign of Olga, nor, I am glad to
say, any mention of Valerie Choade.

It looks like Captain Price's advice was right.

I go round the back to the crazy golf course.

It is a thing of beauty and I am just shaping up for
a putt on the first when a Ford S-Max pulls up in the
drive. Julian gets out with an enormous homosexualist
half his age carrying a man bag and a bottle of
Beaujolais. He is so muscular I am surprised he can
fit in his clothes, let alone the car, and he introduces
himself as Something or Other but I will call him Jim.

I greet them distantly and explain we're going out
for lunch and that Zafira is away for the weekend and we
all jump in one of the fucking people-carriers in the
drive and they strap themselves up and off we go to the
Beijing Gourmet in Chipping Norton.

Since the Chinese occupation of Tibet I am something
of a hero at my local Chinese restaurant. They give us
the best table with a view of the High Street and even

before we've sat down we get prawn crackers and a choice
of lagers.

Jules and Jim take one side of the table and I take
the other.

What with everything else going on, I haven't given
much thought to the fact of having a gay French twin
brother, but now faced with him it hits me with the power
of a dropped piano.

'So, you are French and gay?' I say, more or less
completely recapping our last conversation.

'Oui. And proud of it too.'

The thought of what he might have done to me in our
mother's tummy suddenly hits me. I feel uncomfortable,
and hope my embryonic self had the good sense to sleep
with his back to the womb wall.

'And what about "our" parents? Who are they?'

'Mama is a schoolteacher, and - er - Papa is a folk *Nul*
musician. They have recently moved to live with me *Points!!!*
in Montélimar.'

THE KLAXON FAMILY TREE

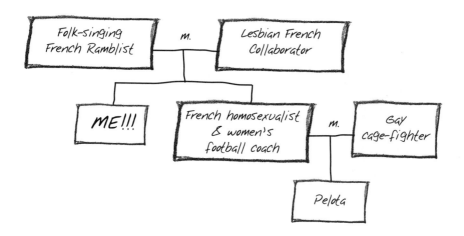

No, really. A schoolteacher and a folk musician.

'Hmmm. What car do they drive?'

'Car? No car. They have always used their bicycles.'

I stare open-mouthed.

'When they are not walking that is,' Jim reminds him.

'Walking?' I ask.

'Yes. La Randonnée. The hiking? You know it?'

'Hmm. I know it. Have you photos?'

'Yes. Right here.'

He takes out a wallet in which are some Euros, three Trojans and a few photographs, including one of Jim looking oiled and dangerous in a bright blue mankini.

'What's that?' I ask.

'Oh, Jim is a - how you say - cage-fighter?'

'Right.'

He shows me the photos.

Dad is straddling a bicycle and wearing a beret and a moustache. He is holding an accordion as if he means to play it. Mum is clearly a lesbian, and she's looking delighted at the prospect of a tune.

'When Jules saw you for the first time on television,' Jim is saying, 'he said it was like looking into the future. You look so much older. I think you have had an interesting life?'

'Well, you could certainly say that at the moment.'

Papa

The noodles arrive.

'So what are you doing now?' I ask, digging in.

'Well,' Jules begins, 'we have just celebrated our civil partnership and Jim is in training for the European Gay Cage-fighting Finals - '

Jim chips in.

'Jules is just being modest. He has recently signed a contract to coach the Arsenal women's team.'

'Oh,' I say, so as not to think about the word Arsenal in connection with whatever these two do with one another after the sun goes down, and probably three or four times before it too.

'Yes, Jeremy, after a successful career with Bordeaux football club I now coach. It is to earn a wage, you understand, but I spend every moment of my free time with Pelota.'

'What's pelota?'

'Pelota is our daughter? Spelled with a silent F and an acute accent on the a.'

MONDAY 20TH SEPTEMBER

State Opening of Parliament. I would have driven up in the new Mercedes XLK and taken my place in the Commons but I've had some flunky from the Department of Fretting Needlessly on the phone and since it turns out that I am actually, legally, French, I am no longer eligible to stand as a member of Parliament.

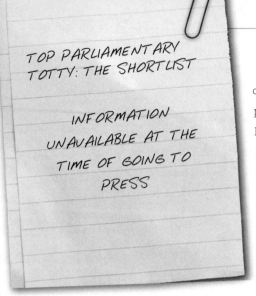

Worse than being denied my chance to represent the good people of Mid-Oxfordshire North-West though, I am now being sent a hundred letters a day from the French department of military affairs who want me to report for basic training at the Toulon naval base. You see, although conscription was suspended in France back in 2001, my three years should have been served in the 1980s, when I was otherwise engaged drinking cider in the White Horse in Parson's Green.

Therefore, their argument goes, I must now proceed to Toulon Naval Academy where I will be taught all I need to know to become a French sailor. I have tried to tell them that thanks to 'Groper' Godson's extensive tutoring in that area, I already know all ANYONE ever needs to become a French sailor, but they're not having it. They have applied for formal extradition and two days ago a policeman dropped around to ask Zafira if she had seen me.

So now it looks as if I'll have to go into hiding.

I have started growing a moustache.

SUNDAY 3RD OCTOBER

Disaster.

Allrite? magazine has started serializing Valerie frigging Choade's memoirs - 'including some sensational

MY COMMANDING OFFICER

revelations about her time on TV's *BottomGear*'. It is unearthly boring so far, and there's no reason the *Mirror* would pay a penny for Valerie's observations on her mother's recipes for chicken soup, or life in Totteridge, so there must be something to come next week.

Totteridge: a typical scene

I ring the photographer who was with Olga and me at Boujis and ask him if I can have copies of the photos he took.

For a small fee he agrees to send them.

Then I take a car for a spin. Just another car, identical to every other I've driven, except a tweak here and a tweak there.

I wonder about personalized number plates after I overtake a van with the number RA34 VAJ. Now vaj is a word that Zafira put on my must-mention sheet a couple of years ago, but it made everyone feel so sick that she's forbidden me to use it again. Seeing this number plate now makes me think that I could give her one for Christmas: MY01 VAJ. It would be a brilliant present.

Like saying 'you are my number one vagina'. Putting it like that does sound a bit odd, I grant you, but I feel sure she'd understand.

When I get home I decide I can't be bothered to write my column and instead play crazy golf until a low mist starts to rise from the hollows and an owl starts to hoot under the purple skies. The stars are out as I pack up, and I wish I'd thought of having some floodlights put in.

// Do I have a novel in me?

WEDNESDAY 6TH OCTOBER

The Pope arrives in his helicopter, Sun Myung Moon in his. Back in the 1970s, before Health and Safety ruined all our fun, kids used to be frightened of quicksand, piranhas, getting shut in fridges and being recruited by the Moonies. Now, though, with these two sitting beside one another on the sofa in the studio, I know whom I am most frightened of. While the Reverend Sun Myung Moon looks as jolly as a retired paedophile, the Pope has eyes so black they actually suck in all the light, and even the Bald Blokes and the Felonious Lesbians are silenced.

'So your Holiness,' I start, 'tell me about the breaking story and the accusations of a cover-up?'

Sun, as I call him, nods and smiles. Not sure he understands. Probably thinking about fried dog, again, because once more we have a Korean with us.

The Pope turns and looks at me and after a long moment draws in a breath.

'Vell,' he says. 'It is all wery wegretable. Instead of coming clean and wecognizing the pwoblem, it was hushed up, and as is alvays the case vhen you do zis sort of thing, it only gets vorse and people - especially the young and the wulnerable - are alvays hurt. For this I am deeply sorry and zere should be an open inquiry into vhat vent vrong, und vhy, and how weparations can be made. The people wesponsible for the fault, and zose guilty in any cover-up, should be held accountable.'

For a moment I am lost for words.

'You'll do all that?' I ask, aware that I have strayed on to some quite serious territory here. It will, I think, teach that log-faced tool Paxman a lesson. 'You're announcing a worldwide investigation into the child abuse scandal?

Then the Pope looks down at something written in the palm of his hand.

'Oh, sorry. I thought you vere talking about ze sticky brake on ze Prius.'

Sun hardly changes his expression, still rocking and smiling.

I give up trying to make this interesting and ask if they'd like to see their race on the telly.

We've bought the Pope a Tiger tank - with which he should be familiar from his youth - and given him a crew of bishops from Argentina, Austria and Belarus, all of whom are equally at home in the back of a tank. The Reverend has Rammond's Hino Poncho, or whatever it is called, the bus he used

LOG-FACED TOOL

on his last challenge, all scraped down one side and
covered in homophobic graffiti we've had a vague stab at
washing off. The master-stroke is to have filled it with
Koreans collected from New Malden and dressed in wedding
outfits as if they are on their way to one of their mass
weddings.

The Pope gets into the driving seat, mashes the gears
to and fro, and then with a roar from the engine and
a plume of smoke even a polar bear could see from his
remaining ice cap, off he goes, straight into the bus
full of Koreans. It is not the best start, I think, but
then I have to thank the Lord we replaced the live
ammunition with paint shells - an idea, I have to say, I
stole from *The World at War*, the BBC series that went on
for almost as long as the war, or *Kelly's Heroes*, one or
the other - because the turret rotates and the gunner
(the Bishop of Belarus or something) fires a perfectly
weighted shot that cracks into the front of the bus,
sending it rocking and dyeing it green. The Koreans
spill out onto the turf half laughing, half crying, their
wedding plans in tatters, and the Prelate of all Austria
opens up on them from his position behind the machine
gun in the tank commander's hatch. Blanks, but still.

How is that for Christian charity?

Then, when the Koreans are scattered and heading home,
leaving their bus covered in various shades of paint,
the tank turns and begins a stately trundle around the
track, with the Austrian waving just as John Paul used
to do from his Popemobile before that Turkish lunatic
shot him. At length the tank rounds Gabon and crosses
the line in under five minutes while the smoking Hino
catches fire behind it on the starting line, and the

Reverend emerges, still smiling, still nodding.

Both men sit there afterwards and watch as the race descends into a farce.

They never really had any beef in the first place, I suppose, so all we have solved is that if the Moonies are faster than the Catholics, the Catholics have all the hardware.

SUNDAY 10TH OCTOBER

I open the pages of the *Allrite?* magazine with more than the ordinary terror and there it is: me smiling at Valerie as if I'd like to cover her in Nutella and spend the rest of the day licking it off. I am outraged because they've cut and pasted her in place of a photograph of Roger Moore taken at the crazy golf course outside Nürburg. Though quite why I was looking at him like that in the first place I can't say. I admire him, that's all, and perhaps I was just relieved he was still alive after our bruising encounter in Crans-Montana.

But that is not the worst of it.

Of course I had been fearing all sorts of disgusting details about our night of sordid passion, but instead there is this:

Exclusive

'MY NIGHT WITH TV'S JEREMY KLAXON'

VALERIE CHOADE DISCOVERS THE MOTOR-MOUTH'S SOFTER SIDE

'He's the sweetest man,' coos Valerie about motor-mouthed heart-throb Jeremy Klaxon, 'and not a bit like he is on the telly.'

'Not like on the telly.'

'We spent the night chatting and spilling our hearts out to each other over a bottle of wine and a selection of cheeses from the hotel dining-room. He told me all about his wife and their love for one another and then he started to cry. He told me his whole life was an act and that if the world could see behind the mask, they would find a caring soul, desperate to be loved. When I asked why he put on his act he said it was because he was afraid of being bullied.

Jeremy had been sent away to boarding-school when he was young and missed his mum and then one night in the dormitory all the boys were talking about their fathers and what they did for a living. One boy said his father was a dentist who drove a Peugeot. The boy pronounced it Pyougeot and everybody laughed at him and that night he wet his bed and two days later the boy had to leave the school because he was being bullied so much. Children can be so cruel!

Jeremy vowed there and then that he would never be caught out like this

Voluptuous Valerie poses in her Totteridge home

34

182

One boy said his father was a dentist who drove a Peugeot

their bond is what keeps him going through all the trials and tribulations. He talks about how much he loves the challenges, when the three of them are away from their families and can finally relax. He told of one night they had spent together in Germany, when they played a game of spin the bottle.

He swore me to secrecy as to what had happened and afterwards he seemed relieved to have got it off his chest. He began sobbing and telling me how much he missed James Might and Richard Rammond. 'I love them, Valerie,' he said, and I really think he meant it.

He began sobbing and telling me how much he missed James Might and Richard Rammond

poor boy and although he did nothing to help him, he decided he would be the biggest bully he could. 'They used to call me Bubbles,' he told me, 'on account of my curly hair, but I soon put a stop to that.' Of course, since he had been put back a year because he failed his exams, being a year older and a foot or two taller than the boys in his class certainly helped!

He is incredibly close to the other members of the *BottomGear* team, and

When we went to Germany to record the outrageous race between the James Bonds he was my knight in shining armour. He was always so considerate of my feelings and would always listen to everything I said. I suppose you could say he is the ultimate gentleman. We shared a room, but nothing happened! I really look forward to the chance of seeing him again and to rekindling our friendship!

35

183

I watch Zafira's face as she is reading this, and I
can see her wondering if this is really the man she
married? When she finishes the paper she folds it up and
leaves it on the table and then, still without saying
anything, she rummages in a drawer and carries something
heavy outside. I reread the article. Minutes later
I hear thumps and bangs and God knows what else and
then after a few minutes I follow her and find she has
destroyed my crazy golf course. The cars are broken,
each one smashed with a lump hammer. The felt is torn
and pulled up and each of my beloved golfist's bats
is bent.

TUESDAY 12TH OCTOBER
Amil turns up in a new Peugeot and I am on the point
of telling him to get it off my land when I see he has
on his serious face - just as he did after I'd used the
word 'vaj' on series ten episode eleventy - and so I
invite him into the kitchen for a cup of Nescaf.

I am right. He has bad news for me, but first I catch
him staring at my moustache.

'What's that?' he asks.

'I admit it isn't very advanced yet, but I thought it
looked quite good.'

'Hmmm. What does Zafira think of it?'

'She likes it.'

He acts surprised.

'Where is she?' he asks.

I tell him she's gone shopping. I think he guessed
otherwise though. Milk bottle on the table. Odd socks.
That sort of thing.

He tells me the police have been around to the track

and the studio and it looks as if the French mean
business about making me serve my national service, or
service militaire, as they would have it. The thought
of a fifty-five-year-old man with a pot belly and a dodgy
hip serving in the French Navy hardly surprises me, but
there is something about this that smacks of revenge for
all the cruel remarks I've made over the years.

'What if everybody I'd ever insulted got up and
started trying to get their own back?'

Neither of us can say anything for a long minute
or two while we ponder the revenge of George Monbiot.
He could come around to my house and bore me to death ✓✓✓
perhaps. *Ha ha!*

'So I've been talking to the BBC solicitors,'
Amil goes on, 'and they say that if you behave
yourself on the next show and review this car -
favourably - and generally be nice about the French then
perhaps they'll let it drop.'

I glance out of the window at the car. There is as

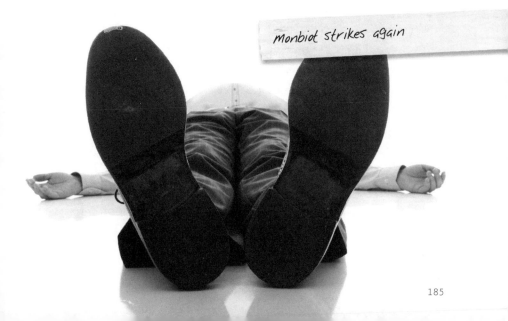

Monbiot strikes again

GAULLIST

always with French cars something a little odd about it, some little niggle with the rest of the world - like doing up your top button, or not joining NATO when the whole organization exists only to protect you - that marks it down as French. It makes me shudder so that my curls quiver.

'And if I can't?' I ask. 'After all my reputation is already in tatters with all Valerie's stuff about me not being half the arsehole I appear to be.'

'Hmmm. She didn't do you any favours, did she?'

For a moment I wonder what sort of favours he has in mind.

'No. I agree.'

'And I hear next week she's going to reveal what really went on in Germany with the truth or dare game?'

'You heard that, did you?'

'I know the editor. But listen, about the extradition. Just lay off the French as a favour to yourself. Otherwise the Christmas Special will be off, James will spend the rest of his life in prison and we'll have to get Quentin Willson to front the show.'

WEDNESDAY 13TH OCTOBER

To the European Gay Cage-Fighting Finals, as a guest of Jules et Jim, at a reconditioned warehouse somewhere in east London. I drive the Peugeot and park where I hope it'll get stolen.

I always assumed that sports like wrestling and rugby were just ways for wardrobe-bound poofs to touch one another without admitting to their wives that they were gay. Not that I would say that to any of them face to face of course, but think about it. You get a team of chaps together, put them in tight shorts and organize for them to rub against one another for 90 minutes and then, when they can stand the tension no longer, you get them into a bath together and make the water so muddy that no one can actually see them putting bars of Imperial Leather up one another's backsides!

It's the same with any of these things that men organize. Trips to Amsterdam aren't really about looking at the hookers, just as fishing trips aren't really about fish, though that's what we tell our wives. It's all about being with other men and hoping that the love that dare not speak its name, to give it its proper name, dares to speak its name.

✓✓✓
Oooh
profound!!!

And so if three men choose to go off on a business trip to Germany, say, and indulge in games of chance involving spinning bottles and so on, well, why not?

EUROPEAN
GAY CAGE-FIGHTING
FINALS

10687661

EUROPEAN
GAY CAGE-FIGHTING
FINALS

Door 4
Row 15
Seat 122

Wed, 13 October 2010
At 20:00
Back door opens at 19:30

£35.00

Is it just me or is this totally Channel Four?!

Some men go to weddings with very real expectations of
rough anal sex with strangers in coat cupboards, so why
shouldn't we organize these little 'boys' trips?

I'm not talking about the *BottomGear* Challenges, of
course.

No homo-erotic tension there at all.

Anyway, anyway, back to the gay cage-fighting. To me
this seems a bit like stopping an orgy to play a game
of Twister, but there you are, and the atmosphere at the
arena is very cheerful, more like an awards ceremony
than a fighting competition. I notice in the audience
a party of men in dinner jackets sitting at a round
table celebrating something. One of them waves to me.
I assume this is a homosexualist thing, and that he is
signalling that he would like to take me home and keep
me as his sex slave. But then I see he is pointing me
out to his friends, who are all turning and beckoning
me over. I dread to think what they have in mind for me

until, looking closer, I see it is Clint Thrust, and next
to him Raoul the director, and next to him, the Austrian
boy with the schlong like a pork loin.

I go over with Jules and introduce them. It turns out
they are celebrating the successful wrapping-up of *In at
the Gay End* by coming to watch the cage-fighting.

'Will you be fighting, Jez?' Clint asks.

I look dumbfounded. Of course I won't be fucking well
fighting, I think, but I see he's serious.

'Oh yeah,' he goes on, 'there's usually a celebrity
bout. Last year it was Davina McCall. I thought it might
be you this year.'

We leave them to it as into the ring come two men,
both nearly naked and each shaved and oiled. Then they
get to it and start butting against one another until
one of them is thrown to the ground and bangs on the mat
to admit he can't take any more.

After two or three rounds Jules comes on, easily
distinguishable from all the other shaved homosexualists
because of his electric blue mankini. He wrestles a
large black chap to the ground and then they get into
an unseemly sprawl during which if you didn't know any
better you'd think it best to look away now. Then there
is another moment when Jules has his thighs around his
opponent's face and it all looks very Channel Four, like
something from *Women in Love* when Ollie Reed and Alan
Bates go at it hammer and tongues. Or do I mean tongs?

Then there is an intermission and I see a short fat
man in a cummerbund come weaving through the tables
towards us. He looks anxious.

I wonder, briefly, if the Peugeot has been stolen. No
such luck.

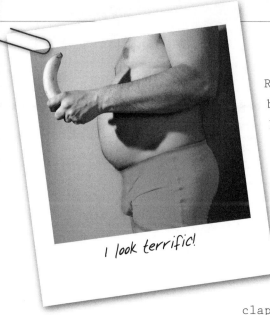

I look terrific!

It turns out that A. A. Roadkill, who was going to be the celebrity wrestler, has hurt his thumb and has had to 'pull out', so would I like the honour of being the guest wrestler?

Only marginally more than being made to chew Holly Johnson's butt plug is my honest answer, but everybody around me is clapping and a spotlight falls on me and there is really nothing I can say that will persuade them I do not want to do it.

Moments later and I am in a dressing room trying to fit myself into a pair of very small electric blue spandex shorts with braces attached and I'm being slathered with a special kind of spermicidal lube.

'You're not in the best shape,' the lubist is telling me, but over his shoulder I see myself in a full-length mirror and think that his eyes must be deceiving him. I look terrific. The shorts are slightly small perhaps, and whatever it is that they are spreading all over my body makes me look like a newborn foal, but I think I look like Germaine Greer.

'Out you go then,' the co-ordinator says, pushing me through the door into the excited crowd who are all on their feet now, wolf-whistling and cat-calling, and for a moment I feel ever so slightly self-conscious, but I make it to the ring where I find a very muscly woman waiting for me.

'I'm not fighting her!' I cry, reasonably enough, 'She's a lesbian!'

Her name is Mary, she tells me in a voice soaked with steroids, and she is going to tear me a new bumhole.

'Yeah, well,' I say, 'I'm going to give you a Chinese burn.'

She turns pale and glances at the referee.

He shrugs as if he has never heard of it.

Meanwhile the continuity announcer tells the audience who we are and why we are here and there is a tremendous stamping of feet. At a table next to us a group of shaved crop-haired lesbians start taking their shirts off to reveal T-shirts suggesting Mary is innocent and should be freed and it reminds me of the good old days when James and Rammond and I used to do *BottomGear* together.

'Remember the rules,' the referee is saying, 'no biting, fish-hooking, eye-gouging, digit manipulation or non-consensual penetration.'

We set to it. We are both so oily that neither can get a good grip on the other. She squirms out of my headlock and tries to flip me, but I grab that bit of hair just in front of her ear and pull her up. Then it gets messy. I have never knowingly been in such close contact with a lesbian's vagina as she attempts to throttle me in the way Xenia Onatopp did

Mary the cage-fighting lesbian

away with that Canadian admiral in *GoldenEye*.

In the end I manage a really old school trick of just lying on her, soaking up the kicks and so on, and using my weight to suppress her. After four minutes of pressure, she gives up and the hall erupts.

I stand up, too late to realize I have a semi, and roar at the crowd.

Once I have tucked my bell-end back into my shorts I am given a medal to hang around my neck. I am just taking the crowd's continued applause when I spot, at the back of the hall, three policemen. I assume they are after Mary, of course, but it turns out they are after me.

Without having time to collect my jeans and shirt, I make a dash for it, leaving Jules and his friends to hold up the boys in blue long enough for me to make it to the side door. When I am out in the cool night air I see a police BMW pulled up at the front door of the venue.

It is so cold my nipples *Ouch!* become erect and get caught on my spandex braces but I race as fast as my dodgy hip will allow me. Never in all my life have I been so pleased to see a Peugeot.

Still not stolen

FRIDAY 15TH OCTOBER

After last night's efforts in the cage I am stiff this morning and get up late. There is still no sign of Zafira, but a man has arrived to repair the crazy golf course and the postman has come with a thick package of photos of my night with Olga Kurylenko. I take them

out and lay them carefully on the kitchen table. There
are some beauties, of course, and three of me kissing
Olga just before the Shaved Chimp slots his stupid head
into the frame. I am not really sure what I hope
to achieve by all this, but part
of my plan is to spoil Valerie's
next serial due on Sunday and so
divert the attention away from her
revelations about the game of truth
or dare in Germany.

   Ordinarily I'd ask Zafira what I
should do, but in her absence Captain
Price remains the next best option.

   After an hour with the scissors
and a pot of glue I have three photos
of me and Olga, and in one of them I
have my hand squarely on her bosom.
Actually it is not my hand, nor is it
her bosom, but that need not matter.
What it is, is what it looks like, as they taught me when
I was learning my trade at *T' Doncaster 'n' Darlington
Echo*, back in the day. In another photo my arm - rather
too long if truth be told, and weirdly octopus-like - is
looping around her back and my hand (actually one I cut
from the front covers of *Mission to Hell* by Taut Kraut,
one of my holiday reads in which a man has to drive a
speedboat across the Mojave Desert), is grasping her
buttock.

   Normally I am a bit rubbish at this sort of thing;
papers and paints and glue and so on. James says it is a
defence mechanism, and that if I show I don't care about
what I'm doing, if I don't look as if I'm trying, then

no one can accuse me of being rubbish, but that is just James.

I wonder what sort of defence mechanisms he's having to put up now?

When I've wiped away all the glue I borrow Zafira's camera and take a photo of the photos. Then I race in the Peugeot to Crappy Snaps in town and have that film developed in an hour.

While I wait I read the *Sun*. There I am on the front page in my spandex microshorts, bellowing in triumph after my cage-fight, and with just the very tip of my knob pixillated. Having my privates thus pixillated is, I decide, just one more thing I have in common with Germaine Greer.

When the photos are done the result is perfection. There I am, clear as day, sharing an intimate moment with Olga Kurylenko.

I roar - in so far as one can roar in a Peugeot - up to London with the photos spread out on the seat next to me, 'Get Ready' by the Temptations on the stereo and singing as I drive: 'I never met a girl who makes me feel the way that you do. (You're alright). Whenever I'm asked who makes my dreams real, I say Kurylenko. (You're outta sight). So, fee-fi-fo-fum, Look out baby, cause I've touched your bum.'

Well - in one of the photos I have.

I am distantly aware of newspaper deadlines, so I drive to the offices of the *Daily Telegraph* and leave the Peugeot on the double yellow lines outside while I go in and demand to see the news editor. It turns out that he was at school with me. I show him the photos. He ums and ahs and worries about ripping up the front page

WIN £50,000

KLAXON SHOWS HIS TODGER!

and starting again. Something about redesign and all the
designers being on holiday or some such.

I offer to take the photos elsewhere.

'You aren't that big a star, Jeremy,' he says. 'And
besides, we could always run the story about what
happened in Germany.'

It seems everybody who is everybody knows about that
night now.

But I am not having any of it. I wave the front page
of the morning's *Sun* under his nose.

'You aren't too old for me to hold upside down in the
toilet again,' I remind him.

Eventually he sees sense.

I don't approve of violence. I think it is undignified,
but sometimes the threat of it applied to someone smaller ✓✓✓
than you is worth trying. He agrees to run the photos *That's*
on the front page the next day in place of something *what I call*
about a far-off earthquake that killed millions. *an ethical*
foreign
policy!!

Once again, no one has stolen the Peugeot.

WEDNESDAY 20TH OCTOBER

Today was what James would call a complete clusterfuck.

Took the Peugeot up to the track to film the piece
for next week's show. After last Saturday's triumph in

the papers there is nothing anyone can do to stop me.
Everybody thinks I am sleeping with Olga Kurylenko and
since she is on holiday somewhere and hasn't heard the
good news yet, I am, for the moment, irrepressible. I hurl
the car around the corners, delighting in the familiar
names - Hampstead, Gabon, Bumfuck - and saying things
like 'not bad for a Cheese-eating Surrender Monkey Car'
and pointing out the teeny amount of understeer. I am
generally straddling the line between being obsequious
and rude that I have worked out with Amil, and that's
when it happens.

It is The Smeg's fault, almost needless to say. I
had forgotten that tomorrow's his birthday, and that
as usual he's having a party. Now some say his parties
are legendary, and that the noise from his thrash metal
band has decimated the wildlife for ten miles in every
direction. Some say the peppers he used in his chilli
last year were the same weapons-grade as used by the
Indian army to quell pro-Pakistani riots. Some say
that this year he is having a French-themed party and
is going to be cooking up a great vat of something

Weapons-grade chilli - the fallout

called tartiflette. Some say he never invites me to these
parties because I am a colossal bore, but all I know
is that as I park the Peugeot, get out, walk across the
tarmac and start my concluding remarks to camera, The
Smeg makes his appearance in a van borrowed from a local
delicatessen.

'So this Peugeot is a surprise,' I am saying. 'It has
all the joie de vivre you would expect from a French car,
and a little bit more. This car,
then, is Carla Bruni.
This car is Carla Bruni if /////
she were washed and dried *One of*
my best!
and drizzled all over with
lavender-scented truffle oil,
and had an afternoon free to
see her favourite motoring
journalist, this car is - '

Lubricated

And it is just as I am
uttering these immortal
words and looking back
at the car and actually
beginning to salivate that
The Smeg hurls the delicatessen van round the corner and
rams straight into the Peugeot's side panels, lifting the
car off the ground so that it turns over in mid-air and
lands on its roof.

There is an ear-splitting explosion.

Dark things fly up into the air with a hard whistle of
escaping gas, then come raining down on us as we race for
cover.

Amil is knocked to the ground by something heavy
and round. It looks like a cheese. It *is* a cheese.

Then another lands and Amil, already
prostrate, takes a crottin de chèvre in
the knackers. A whole brie, spinning
lethally, nearly decapitates the
girlchild, while I narrowly avoid being
kebabbed by a cured sausage that whizzes
down like an RPG and embeds itself phallicly
in the turf. Natasha's face is obliterated in an
explosion of gooey Vacherin.

Then the cameraman takes one on the foot from a small
hard object: an onion.

A side of bacon lands next to me as if it has fallen
from the bomb bay of a B-52 Stratofortress.
Then suddenly bulbs of garlic and
onions are thumping down and bouncing
all around us and then come more
cheeses - huge great blocks of the stuff
- and potatoes and great vats of cream
and blocks of butter. It is as if
we are being attacked by the French.
So this, I think, is how they won the
battle of... the battle of... no,
where was it? I simply can't remember a
single battle that was won by the French. Crécy? No,
that was us. Agincourt? No, that was us too. What about
Trafalgar? The Nile? Blenheim? No. No. No.

All the while the camera rolls as the Peugeot and the
van - the logo says The Smeg has borrowed it from a shop
called La Fromagerie - begin to burn. After a moment,
The Smeg steps out of the cab of the van and walks away
into his garage. There is another explosion as one of
the gas canisters goes up. The Peugeot and the van are

torn apart and all that is left is a twisted heap of
blackened French metal, some potatoes, garlic, onions,
cheese and bacon.

'Oh dear,' I say. 'That wasn't meant to happen.'

But I have had so many cars set alight, crushed with
pianos, dropped in acid, launched from trebuchets etc etc
that having The Smeg drive a van full of France's finest
into a Peugeot just looks like another stupid stunt,
albeit not as good as any of the others. And now I stand
there and nothing I do can make me look sincerely sorry.

SATURDAY 6TH NOVEMBER

On the seventh day, God rested, and the devil got up and
made this place. No, it's not Detroit, it is even worse.
It's Pwllheli, or something like that, in
Wales and I am stuck here in a caravan
park in the rain. A yard away from
my window is another caravan, filled
with teenaged ginger Scousers, also, I
think, on the run from the police.

Up yours, Charlotte Church!

I've been here since the Peugeot
blew up and the French decided they
definitely want me for basic training in
Toulon. The next day the police descended
on my house and I was lucky to get away on a quad bike
over the fields to Chipping Norton. They weren't allowed
to follow me because of Health and Safety issues,
apparently, and so here I am, on the run, holed up in
James Might's caravan.

The police aren't the only ones after me either.
Journalists are all over the place trying to get my
story. Olga eventually turned up and denied she'd ever

I'd rather Dai

even met me. Her boyfriend - not the sort of chap you'd want to be messing with - has sent his own 'security people' to find me and take me, as far as I can gather, to his dacha near Murmansk.

The rain has not stopped for a week and I have had to wear one of James's cagoules to visit the Spar to buy leeks and turnip bread. Thank God for my moustache - without it I'm certain the one-eyed shopkeeper would know who I am. The wet weather has helped in that department, and now when I look in the shaving mirror I see a curly-headed Magnum P.I.

But it has not all been gloom and doom. Zafira has been in touch after seeing the photos of me having my spandex wardrobe malfunction after the cage-fight. She said she thought I looked very sexy, but more importantly the Japanese have gone for my 'Jeremy's Garage' idea. I'd rather forgotten about it with all the standing for parliament nonsense, but now I see that television is my natural home, not the House of Commons, even if it is Japanese television. Crucially, I would have to film it in Japan, which would mean I could avoid the French extradition order, if not Olga's boyfriend's men.

Zafira says she will come back to me, even to the caravan here in Pwllheli on condition that I make the HomeGrown™ adverts. She has sent me the ideas and I must

say, after what I have been through recently, they seem
reasonably dignified.

If I weren't in a caravan I might get a semi at the
thought, but no one ever got an erection in a caravan. √√√

*Good enough for the Oxford
Dictionary of Quotations?*

THURSDAY 18TH NOVEMBER

Haven't spoken to a single human being - if you discount
the Scousers and the shopkeeper, which I do - for two
weeks, but I've discovered a nine-hole crazy golf course
down by the beach. It is not so
fine as mine, of course, and the
theme is entirely random. It also
takes a little getting used to
and, like all links courses, it
slopes towards the sea. I went
around twice today in the rain
until the lightning started and
the lunatic who otherwise spends
his time in the booth with one
finger up his nose and the other
- attached to the others on his
hand - down his pants came out
wearing a shiny tabard and put
a bollard over the first hole and told me the course
was now closed 'for health and safety reasons'.

Twat

Cunt.

MONDAY 22ND NOVEMBER

Dreamt that Rammond has been asked to cover for me on
BottomGear.

When I go to the Spar to buy more Nesquik I discover
in the *Mail* that it's true.

Well, at least it's not Quentin Willson.

The whole world seems to be at war, I notice. Greenland has declared war on Denmark (good), France on Andorra (should be close), Guinea on Equatorial Guinea and Guinea-Bissau (who knows?), Peru on Chile, Chile on Argentina, Argentina on Peru, and on it goes. I ring Zafira from the phone box. She tells me she's dealing with the French authorities over the extradition proceedings.

'Can't they take Rammond instead?' I ask.

'Is possibility.'

'What about the Russians?'

'Fucking Russians!'

I should never have asked.

FRIDAY 26TH NOVEMBER

A car arrives at dawn. I think it is the Russians and for a moment I think I am going to need a new pair of pyjama bottoms, but it is Zafira.

'Come quick,' she says, shrugging out of my halitotic embrace, 'and wear these.'

She hands me a red cloak with a white fur trim on the hood, a pair of matching red trousers, black boots and a thick black belt with a big gold buckle. I put them on and she bundles me into the back of the car. It is still dark. She lingers in the caravan for a moment. When she emerges, she closes the door very carefully.

I don't know it then, but this is the last time I'll ever see the caravan.

Actually it is more or less the last time *anyone* will ever see the caravan again, because although I had been congratulating myself on finally visiting a caravan park without setting anything on fire, it turns out that Zafira set a booby trap in James's caravan to 'discourage' the Russians.

When they finally open the door, an hour or so later, the thing goes up in a ball of fire, flame-grilling one of them, wounding two others and, incidentally, taking my quad bike with it. I never find out what happened to the Scousers. Not sure anyone really cares.

Then we speed off, retracing my route back to England.

'Where are we going? I ask Zafiira.

'Pinewood,' she says, glancing at me from the corner of her eye. 'What is thing on lip?'

It turns out that today we're shooting the HomeGrown™ advert.

It is only when I get there that I notice I am dressed as Father Christmas. Once I've donned a white beard and had someone stick some fur on the top of my head to cover my bald spot, I sit in a motorized sledge parked on top of a roof for an hour or two, waiting for two children to complete their lines:

Child A: 'Is that *BottomGear*'s Jeremy Klaxon?'

Child B: 'No! It's Santa!'

Child A: 'But Santa isn't bald!'

Then I take my hood off, revealing my fabulous head of curls and luxuriant beard, and I say:

'Thanks to HomeGrown™, neither am I!'

And then I roar away in my mechanical sledge, the engine of which is so loud and powerful that the snow falls off the roof, covering the two boys in a three-foot drift. It makes no formal sense but there you are. It's a living.

WEDNESDAY 1ST DECEMBER

Open the first door of my *BottomGear* advent calendar with a chocolate car behind each door. Today's is rather vague: some sort of mid-level saloon that looks faintly Hunnish. A BMW 3 series? Or an Audi? It is red, anyway, and the chocolate tastes of pig fat.

Then it is up the studio in a rented bullet-proof Lexus LX470. The French have dropped their extradition proceedings against me but the Russians are still out there and so I have to drive a Lexus for security reasons. It costs me two litres of diesel just to get to the end of the drive (where they've replaced the speed bump, now that I am no longer MP for Mid-Oxfordshire North-West) and the stereo is permanently set to Al-Jazeera news, but it gives you a certain sense of

You can't get me now, George Monbiot!

solidity. It is so solid I don't even notice when I run down cyclists and pram-pushers.

When I get to the studio Amil tells me we are going to have to drop the We Can Solve Every Problem in the World by Racing Around the

Track in Reasonably Priced Cars. This is apparently for
health and safety reasons, because so many countries
are starting wars with their neighbours so that their
presidents can be invited to resolve their differences
on the show. Amil estimates that more than 15,000 lives
have been lost and untold billions of pounds' worth of
damage caused in an epidemic of border disputes. Well,
it just goes to show that you ought not to try to help
anyone, but stick to what you know.

We are starting work on the 'other' Pink Panther
today, the one we're going to pretend to build ourselves
for the purposes of blowing up or setting on fire or
crashing into a bus full of gingers and it will be the
first time I've seen Rammond since July. When I do I
am astonished to see that he's shrunk. Perhaps it's
some deal he has struck with Baron
Samedi? For every new series he is
given, he loses an inch in height.

He is complimentary about my
moustache, though, and tells me I
look like a young Peter Mandelson.

'Not Magnum, P.I.?'

He squints.

'Maybe in the half-light.'

Despite myself a tear comes
into my eye and when he
terrorist-fist-bumps me and
bumps his shoulder to mine,

I moustache you not to mention it. Ho, ho!

I cannot help but hug his wiry little
body to my own. Physical contact feels good. Zafira is
still sleeping in another room - even though she knows
I didn't shag Valerie or Olga - and the last person to

Rammond's mum - even shorter than Rammond!!

touch me in any meaningful way was Mary the cage-fighting lesbian.

Then, after a moment, we are back to insulting each other's mothers before Amil, now looking greyer at the temples since I last saw him, arrives to start organizing the day's shooting.

We've got part of the chassis from a Ford van and a drawing of one of the original Pink Panthers. The idea is to film us using the two tools we have - a hammer and a spot-welding machine - to knock together various bits of old scrap. Then I'll splodge it with pink paint before, metaphorically speaking, we fuck off down the pub.

The fact that the resulting vehicle is utterly rubbish is the entire point, of course. The worse the job, the better the telly. With luck we'll burn the warehouse down or flood Godalming and in the end we want whatever we make to be as lethal as a Jihadist in a ✓✓✓ ball-bearing factory.

This kind of gag looks simple, and you might say we're making a virtue out of necessity, but how many other telly programmes do it like this? Imagine if they did it on *Blue Peter*? A coked-up young presenter (probably disabled) staggering around the 'craft table' pouring glue everywhere and pretending that it didn't matter if the balloon head they were making ended up looking like Adolf Hitler or Fred West or Simon Weston.

MONDAY 6TH DECEMBER

So here we go, off on our jaunt to rescue James. I am
in a brand new Land Rover, painted pink, with all the
unnecessary elements - doors and windows and lights and
so on - removed and replaced by things you might not
ordinarily expect to find in a 4WD. Along with ten - TEN!
- jerry cans of petrol, there are brackets for things
such as machine guns, grenade launchers, mines, smoke
bombs and searchlights, which we're going to collect
from Nikolai in Venice, since the EuroReichists won't let
us travel on the motorway without luminous jackets, let
alone carrying enough military hardware to sink Belgium.

There is even one for something called a MILAN wire-
guided missile system, though since this last is named
after an Italian city, it's probably a bit temperamental,
smells of sewage and wakes you up at three in the
morning with the noise of a teenager on a motor scooter
whose silencer fell off years ago on his way home after
an unsatisfactory night dry humping his girlfriend while
she's trying to do the ironing, outside, watching the
football on a telly placed, for no very good reason, on a
bracket eight feet in the air.

My Land Rover is based on the Defender, so it has a
2495cc engine capable of delivering 122bhp and a top
speed of 87mph, but since its tyres are as knobbly as the
Singing Detective's face, it can only reach about 70 mph.

It is, in a word, crap.

Rammond's, though, is even worse.

As we make our way out of the studio I can see him -
if I turn my head, since the mirrors have been taken away
- chugging in a cloud of diesel fumes and flying sparks.
Something is dragging along behind the vehicle and bits

keep falling off. At this rate he'll never get there in time for the live Christmas Special.

It's all my fault, of course, because every time Rammond or one of the studio chimps added something to the car, like an engine, or a steering wheel, I'd come along and knock it off with my hammer. I was, you see, very keen not to have to drive a car made in the *BottomGear* studios all the way to Istanbul.

I was pretty keen not to have to drive any kind of car all the way to Istanbul, to tell you the truth, but on the way back from the studio the other night I was followed by a car full of Russian security advisors, and so discretion being the better part of valour, I thought I'd take this opportunity to get out of the country for a bit.

A dreary gusset-nuzzler

So here we are, chugging along with all the panache of a medium-sized block of council flats and, thanks to the dreary gusset-nuzzlers in Brussels, who won't let our made-up Pink Panther on the motorways, we're going via the scenic route, down to Newhaven and across to Dieppe.

We only just make the crossing. At the last minute Rammond comes sweeping down the ramp into the port and I have to say that his car now looks pretty good. It is basically the chassis of an old Ford van with the body cut off at about chest height.

We took the doors off, but left the windscreen and then painted the thing pink. Well, pinkish. Rammond is wearing driving goggles and a tea-towel on his head, but still manages to get through customs without too much mugging to camera.

Now I haven't been on a ferry since the Queen's Silver Jubilee when communists ruled the country and a tattooed lady with one arm was sick down the front of my trousers, but even I am surprised at how little has changed.

Or perhaps it's not so much the ferries that haven't changed as the people who use them.

They're still by some way the ugliest people in the world, ever.

Honestly. It's as if someone went around collecting up anyone who'd been run over by a Fiat Multipla and shipped them aboard. Anne of Cleves? Tick. John Merrick? Tick. Shane MacGowan? Tick. The cast of *Coronation Street*? Tick. Christ, Susan Boyle's marginally less attractive sister would be a beauty queen on this Channel crossing. ///

More alarmingly still, on this ferry there is also an area called, and I kid you not, The Road Kings Drivers

Club. It is reserved exclusively for lorry drivers, and
I think we all know what goes on in there, don't we?

I can almost hear the screams.

But that is not for us.

No. We are with the masses in the all-you-can-eat-
for-£5 lounge, sharing our table with about fifteen Poles
with close-set eyes, shaven heads, necks like oil drums
and skin like salt and vinegar crisps - and that's just
the women. The men are all wearing leather coats and
they've tucked their patterned jumpers into their jeans
so that it looks as if they have just been disturbed
while having a crap.

Thanks to my moustache and full head of hair - all
down to Homegrown™ - no one recognizes me and I am
allowed the luxury of a little time to plan our route.
For this I have a motorway map and a book called *Tous
les campings de France*, because in honour of the brave
boys of the SAS we have not booked into any hotels or
bed and breakfasts, but will instead be camping.

TUESDAY 7TH DECEMBER

First night camping not so good. Pitched our tent in
a horrible little motorway siding called the Aire de
Sarkozy-les-Deux-Fromages or something, and find out that
we're much too close to the urinals. Not only was the
smell abysmal - I thought it was Rammond for most of the
night - but we kept on being disturbed by lorry drivers
slashing loudly in the zinc urinals and telling each
other tales of murdering prostitutes.

Camping has always been
a pet subject with us on
BottomGear, and in the past
we've used caravanners and
campists as shorthand for
a certain type of person at
whom it is easy to laugh, and
for that, of course, we aren't
remotely sorry.

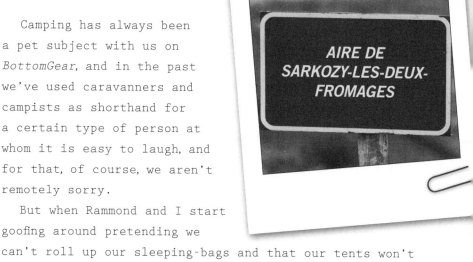

But when Rammond and I start
goofing around pretending we
can't roll up our sleeping-bags and that our tents won't
come down, Amil cuts it short.

'This kind of thing only works when James is around,'
he says.

We groan and get back into our cars and set off.

It is a hell of a long way to Istanbul when you can
only do 70 mph. If we steer clear of motorways - which
we have to - the trip is about eleventy million miles.
If we drive at a steady 70 mph, I estimate that the
journey will take us 274-and-a-half hours.

Obviously, though, we'll need to make stops along the
way so that we can reinforce national stereotypes and
poke fun at people who can't speak English or have never
seen an episode of *Big Brother*. We also have to build in
time for Rammond's Pink Panther to catch fire and explode,
taking with it some architectural gem or other that the
RAF missed. And then there will be the highly amusing
attempts at camping, the run-ins with officials, the
problems with paying for petrol in a foreign language,
the differences in the sorts of chocolate they sell, and
the availability of beer at motorway service stations.

OPERATION LAZY RACIST GENERALIZATION:
THE ITINERARY

LAND

LAND

LAND

SEA

BELGIUM
Corrupt paedophiles,
Wide range of beers

GERMANY
Square-headed
war-losers,
Good but
uninspiring
cars

London

FRANCE
Garlic-infused
cheesemakers,
War-losing
homosexualists

AUSTRIA

Venice

SERBIA
Yugos

Leather-short
wearers,
vegetablist
dictators

ITALY

GREECE

Istanbul

TURKEY
Hummus-eating
semi-towelheadists,
Decent kebabs

Corinth
Canal

Corruption,
Men in women's
underwear,
Women with
moustaches,
Alfa Romeo 166,
Olive oil

SEA

Fiscally inept
ouzo-drinkers

We are due to meet Nikolai in Venice on the 17th, by
which time we will have driven through and laughed at:

France and the French: oily, garlic-infused, sex-mad
mummy's boys who'd rather serve Chateaubriand and Veuve
Clicquot to the Wehrmacht than serve in their own paltry   √√√√
little army.   *Definitely*
                                                            one for the
Belgium and the Belgians: Hopeless paedophiles.   *ST column*
No motoring history of which to speak. Behaved
badly in the Congo. Corrupt, ugly, base and unreliable:
the Italians of the north.

Germany and the Germans: Square-headed war-losers.
Makers of boring but very good cars and rugs. Now
relentlessly worthy, with a Green Party that has an
envirosexual policy that might be more dangerous than
the National Socialist doctrine of *Lebensraum*.

Austria and the Austrians: Basically the same as
the Germans, but worse. Without any sense of guilt or
the cars. The nastiest people in Europe by some margin,
cellar dwellers and world champion-wearers of leather
shorts and braces.

Italy and the Italians: Plenty of soul, yes, but
unreliable. The men are cowardly embezzlers and the
women on time-delay fuses to quadruple in size the
moment they get a ring on their finger. There is a joke
about fingers and rings here that a more amusing man than
I might make, so I shan't. Easily the most venal and
pathetic country in Europe, and I love it there.

THURSDAY 16TH DECEMBER
Fuckbucket!

It wasn't Rammond's car that exploded. It was mine! I
never bothered to fill it with oil or something and the

fucking thing got really hot, seized up, caught fire and
then blew up just by some old church as we were waiting
by the harbour. Rather unfortunately the explosion
brought down the church wall, causing millions of
pounds' worth of improvements to the place.

The PC brigade won't like that, and nor, it turns out,
will *La Polizia*, who can sniff out the chance to extract
a bribe from a red-blooded Englishman at 3,000 paces.

Thankfully Nikolai's boat's in the harbour already,
and he's unloaded his cigarettes and trafficked his
prostitutes and so we load up. Rammond's pretend Pink
Panther goes first, followed by the two Range Rovers full
of cameramen and their equipment. For such a fast boat,
Nikolai's boat carries a huge cargo.

Anyway, we leave Natasha behind to distract the
Italians in any way she can and we set sail a day ahead
of schedule, aiming for Istanbul via the Corinth Canal
just as the sound of the police sirens reaches us.

This kind of thing never happens to Daniel Craig.

FRIDAY 17TH DECEMBER
At sea off Croatia, I think. Quiet start to the day
spent fixing up Rammond's Pink Panther. We've more or
less copied the exact attachments I had on mine, and
thanks to Nikolai's contacts we now have a full on-board
armoury to set up. We try our new weapons out on various
other vessels and marine life as we go. The Miniguns
are multi-barrelled machine guns that fire trillions of
rounds per second and they can cut a fishing boat from
bow to stern in one careful pass.

Fantastic fun - but not as good as the MILAN
missiles.

I've fired these things in *Call of Duty*,
of course - to hit helicopters from the
White House roof, for example - and
in fact firing the real thing is
frighteningly similar. They are
expensive though, and Amil only
lets us have one practice
shot each. I go first and
we all stand and watch
as the missile hurtles
across the sea until it
is no more than a dot and
Rammond says, 'Ooh, I don't think
you want to be doing that!'- which makes me want to do
it all the more - and then there is a small mushroom of
flame and a column of dark smoke on the shore.

Nikolai tells me I have just hit some old library in
Dubrovnik.

'Whoops!' I say, and we all laugh.

SATURDAY 18TH DECEMBER

Woken by searchlights in the dark. It seems the
Croatians have taken exception to our entirely
unprovoked assault on their so-called 'Jewel of the
Adriatic'. They've sent their navy after us, and
something tells me they aren't after our autographs.
They came up on our stern yesterday afternoon, three MTBs
that made me think of dear old 'Groper' Godson and the
English Democrats. Nifty seamanship on Nikolai's part
allowed us to give them the slip, and we headed south,
but then Rammond spotted them closing on us again.

'We're in Greek waters!' Nikolai shouted, but you

could see from his face that this was bad news. I must have hit a world-class monument in Dubrovnik.

'Rammond!' Nikolai yells. 'Get on the Minigun! Keep those boats away!'

It's just like *Call of Duty*!

Rammond is quickly up in the back of his truck. The gun pokes over the gunwale of the boat and Rammond stands behind it and starts to spray our pursuers with bullets while Amil signals to the cameramen to keep rolling.

'Jez?' Nikolai says. 'We'll have to use another MILAN. But wait until we are in the canal. Then we can get them more easily.'

I grab the MILAN controls again. Someone has already loaded the missile into its housing and I feel the stirrings of a significant boner.

We crash through the harbour of an idyllic fishing village, scattering smaller boats in our wake and then we are into the Corinth Canal - one of the very few things of note that the Greeks have built since the Acropolis. As we tear up the canal its walls rise higher and higher until they tower over our heads. We are speeding between cliffs that we could reach out and touch if we weren't in so ball-busting a hurry.

And if we weren't being chased by some very angry Croats with guns and names such as Goran, Vuk, Slavoj and Slobodan. Not men you necessarily want to be messing with, especially if they are armed with some very serious military hardware and you've just destroyed their most famous monument.

Then Nikolai nods and I let fly with the MILAN.

Of course it misses the boat.

But it does hit the rock wall above us. And a great wedge of rubble breaks off. It slides down into the canal, just in front of the lead boat, blocking it so completely that not even the most determined eel could get through.

'Hold on tight!'

From under the cloud of debris and dust comes a towering wave of green water. I scream. It hits us and we tip nose down. For one horrible moment it seems we are going to be upended, but Nikolai in the driving seat puts a touch of gas on the throttle and the boat

Nikolai

adjusts, rights itself, and we level out, ten feet higher than we ought to be, but level none the less. Rammond is squealing with delight - he has never been this high before and the lack of oxygen makes him giddy - while my semi has bloomed to a full-on javelin.

This is what coming under fire is all about. This is a feeling Captain Price would know exactly.

The walls of the canal fizz past our noses and we are all grinning like madmen when we burst out into the sunshine and blue waters of the Aegean Sea.

It is true that in the last three or four days we have destroyed a fifteenth-century Venetian church, burned Dubrovnik to the ground (again) and now broken one of the engineering marvels of the world, but we have touched greatness, and nothing now will stop this mighty *BottomGear* adventure turning out to be the best yet.

Corinth Canal c2010, <u>after</u> BottomGear Christmas Special

THURSDAY 23RD DECEMBER
Istanbul.

Another good one for the show

If Istanbul were a car, it would be a cut-and-shut mash-up between a Rolls-Royce Silver Spur and something like a Chevy flatbed truck. √√ The front - the European side - is massive and opulent, like the wood-panelled splendour that is a Rolls-Royce interior, but the back - the Asian side - is functional and smells as if they have been using their own wee to tan leather for centuries, which they have.

On the one hand it is lucky that James's prison is on the European side of the Bosphorus, but on the other a car like ours still attracts a certain amount of attention. And, as we drive it off Nikolai's boat - giving him in payment for his services the exact amount Jonathan Ross earns in a year - we are soon surrounded by children trying to get Rammond's signature.

How they recognize him I cannot say, for we have all changed these last few weeks. Our diet of mud and sphagnum moss has left us leaner than before, and we are darkly tanned. Even Rammond has managed a beard of sorts. We are now wearing worn combat shirts, tea-towels on our heads and steel welders' goggles against the glare of the sun. We look mean, we look tough, we look, dare I say it, exceedingly gay. √

I no longer look like a testicle-faced old lesbian.

No. I look like Magnum in those even then frankly incredible flashbacks to Vietnam, when he and his buddies Rick and T.C. used to pass their R&R shooting gooks from the back of a helicopter.

As we drive through the centre of Istanbul it is as if we are liberating Paris. Cowardly-looking men stop and stare at us as we make our way in convoy up through the town. Women in unsuitable dresses flash their private parts at us (well, they don't actually). The camera crews are in the Range Rovers, in front and behind us, taking in the photogenic sights as we go, and it seems incredible that this is going out live.

Anything could happen.

I mean, literally, anything.

You see, we haven't really got a plan.

I hold up my arm and Rammond applies the brake next to a toothless crone selling barbecue fans at the roadside. Something falls off the van.

'Sagmalcilar prison?' I ask.

She's no help and so on we go.

No map: toothless and useless

What is this? Where I live everybody knows where everything is and if you stop to ask someone, say, the way to the knacker's yard, or where you can buy some cobnuts, you'll get an honest answer.

Not here though. Not in Istanbul.

Eventually a man jumps onto the running board. Mustafa's a greasy little chap with a

bristly moustache and camel's teeth. He gives us the
usual run-around - if you want a flea-pit hotel, or out-
of-focus pictures of a chubby belly dancer who's clearly
never seen a bar of soap or a razor, or a cousin who owns
a taxi, or a defence of what happened to the Armenians
('they slipped') and what is happening to the Kurds
('they keep slipping') then he's your man. But he does
tell us something interesting. Sagmalcilar, the prison
in which James Might has apparently been rotting since
whenever, was closed down in 2008.

'So where is he?' we ask. After all, we've come all
this way.

'You maybe try Sultanahmet prison.'

'Is that near here?'

'Oh yes. Very near.'

We look at one another and
then shrug, as you do.

We take a few turns and
follow a busy road until we
pull up at what, to my mind,
looks nothing like a Turkish
prison.

mustafa

'Mustafa, you clod, this is
a hotel for God's sake, not
a prison.'

It is in fact the Four
Seasons Hotel Istanbul.

It is frankly typical of
James not to be where he is supposed to
be. It would not now surprise me if indeed he were in
a different country.

But the problem is that the Four Seasons just looks

too inviting for men who have spent the best part of the last month on the boat.

'Shall we just have a quick drink?' I ask Amil.

'This is going out live, Jez! We only have an hour to find James.'

'But just one drink, Amil! It'll be funny! It'll make us look irresponsible!'

'And it'll be a waste of licence payers' money!'

Quarter of an hour later we are guzzling champagne and wearing white towelling bathrobes. I am having a manicure from a plump little Turkish beauty - all five foot one of her - while a bald man with a pair of luxuriant moustaches is removing Rammond's wispy beard with a cut-throat razor.

'The thing is, Jez,' he is saying, 'my agent told me that with James out of the country there's bound to be more work for me. I mean, I actually went up for that series he did on toys and lego.'

'It would have taken them about ten minutes to build a lego house for you,' I say.

'Exactly. That would've saved hundreds of thousands of the licence payers' pounds.'

'Which we could spank on Lambos!'

'And trips to Oz, or the Bahamas!'

'And more drinks!'

A waiter arrives and fills our glasses.

The cameramen keep filming.

'So what you are saying, Rammond, is that it would be doing everyone a favour if we just left James here?'

Fatima: the plump little Turkish beauty

'That's it, exactly. I mean, what does he bring to the party?'

I think about what happened in Germany. With Might permanently incarcerated, there is one person less left to talk about it. Perhaps Rammond's agent is right, too, that there would be more work for us without him and his absurd shows.

'And if we were in his shoes - hey, you could easily sleep in one of them - then would he come and rescue one of us?'

There is a pause. Has it come to this? We've driven all this way, only to fail? It wouldn't be the first time, of course, and in fact we've always prided ourselves on being a bit crap.

'So shall we just tell Amil we're not going to bother to save James?' I ask Rammond.

'We could do,' he says. 'Since we've only got a few minutes left of this show.'

I glance at my GIANT watch.

'All right,' I say, 'let's do it.'

I turn to the camera, where Amil is looking ashen-faced, and I raise my newly topped-up glass.

'And on that bombshell, ladies and gentlemen, it's time to say good night and happy Christmas, and a *BottomGear* New Year.'

PICTURE CREDITS

p34 Bryn Pinzgauer/Flickr; p35 AFP/Getty Images; p45 Li Tao Xinhua/Xinhua Press/Corbis (the King of all China only); p47 Max Smith; p54 John Springer Collection/Corbis (head of Lawrence of Arabia); p60 Franklin McMahon/Corbis; p81 Gray Mortimore/Getty Images; p84 Rune Hellestad/Corbis; p86 Davis Boulton/ Getty Images; p95 Patrick Seeger/dpa/Corbis (Moore's head); p117 Andy Rain/ epa/Corbis; pp132-133 WPA Pool/Getty Images; p138 Tony Korody/Sygma/Corbis; p141 General Photographic Agency/Getty Images; pp148-149 Peter Andrews/Corbis (Dalton), Patrick Seeger/dpa/Corbis (Moore), Robert Kenney/Retna Ltd/Corbis (Lazenby); p151 Sunset Boulevard Corbis; p155 Sunset Boulevard/Corbis; p161 David Moir/Reuters/Corbis; p166 Sashenka Gutierrez/epa/Corbis; p169 Moore/Getty Images p171 Rune Hellestad/Corbis (Piers Morgan only); p179 Colin McPherson/Corbis (Paxman's head); p205 David James/Sygma/Corbis (Magnum P.I.'s head)

First published in hardback in Great Britain in 2010 by Atlantic Books, an imprint of Atlantic Books Ltd.

Copyright © Toby Clements, 2010

The moral right of Toby Clements to be identified as the author of this work has been asserted by him in accordance with the Copyright, Designs and Patents Acts of 1988.

1 2 3 4 5 6 7 8 9

A CIP catalogue record for this book is available from the British Library.

ISBN: 978 184887 724 5

Produced for Atlantic Books by Essential Works, Ltd

www.essentialworks.co.uk

Printed in Great Britain by the MPG Books Group

Atlantic Books
An imprint of Atlantic Books Ltd
Ormond House
26-27 Boswell Street
London
WC1N 3JZ

www.atlantic-books.co.uk